SOME ASPECTS OF THE
NATURAL HISTORY
OF THE FOLKESTONE
DISTRICT

SOME ASPECTS OF THE

NATURAL HISTORY

OF THE FOLKESTONE DISTRICT

Published to mark the

CENTENARY

*OF THE FOLKESTONE
NATURAL HISTORY SOCIETY
FOUNDED* 4 APRIL 1868

Copyright © 1968
FOLKESTONE NATURAL HISTORY SOCIETY
Printed in Great Britain by
Headley Brothers Ltd
THE INVICTA PRESS Ashford Kent

This book was produced with the
collaboration of staff & students of
FOLKESTONE SCHOOL OF ART
Design & typography: Graham S. Hudson ATD
Maps & diagrams for Chapters 2 & 3: Andrew Austin
Maps illustrating Chapter 16: Karl Pitwon

CONTENTS

PREFACE

Members of Folkestone Natural History Society felt that the Society's Centenary should be marked by a more ambitious publication than had been attempted by them in recent years. It was clearly not possible for any one member to cover the whole field of local natural history, nor was the Society in a position to commission such a work. It was therefore decided to ask a limited number of members and friends of standing in various fields to contribute an article under the general editorship of a special committee of the Society. Contributors were free to write as they chose, the only briefing being that articles should be of general interest to the intelligent amateur who is curious, who likes to know, to explore, and to contemplate the subtle interplay of factors which lead to the individuality of a region, its landscape, fauna and flora. A brief history of the Society has been included by way of introduction. The preparation of this was entrusted to the Honorary Secretary who had a complete set of minutes, publications and records going back to the Society's founding date, 4th April 1868.

The committee were greatly encouraged in their scheme by a substantial donation from Messrs Pfizer Ltd; by technical advice and assistance from the Principal and Staff of Folkestone and Dover Schools of Art; by the ready loan of electros by Shell-Mex & BP Ltd for the plate *Dungeness Bird Sanctuary* reproduced from the Shell Bird Book by permission of Ebury Press and Michael Joseph, and by the Central Electricity Generating Board for those of moths;

and finally by permission of *The Times* to reproduce the article entitled 'Romney Marsh, its subtle and changing beauty'. Blocks or illustrations have kindly been loaned by Mr A. Clough, Miss A. D. Long, Mrs M. H. Walton, Mr G. H. Youden, Central Electricity Generating Board, *Folkestone Herald*, Forestry Commission, Kent Trust for Nature Conservation, Nature Conservancy, Skyfotos Ltd, and World Wildlife Fund. Students of Folkestone School of Art have drawn various maps and diagrams to ensure uniformity of style. Sincere appreciation is expressed to all these, to the contributors of articles, and to the many others who have in any way assisted in the work.

Vera F. P. Day NDH

1

FOLKESTONE NATURAL HISTORY SOCIETY

'A meeting of gentlemen interested in the study of Natural History was held in the Town Hall, by kind permission of the Mayor, on 4th April, 1868, Dr. C. E. Fitzgerald, M.D., in the Chair.'

Thus, according to the first minute book, Folkestone Natural History Society came into being one hundred years ago. Dr Fitzgerald was appointed President, and Mr H. Ullyett BSc, Honorary Secretary. The minutes stated further, 'The whole of the gentlemen present then gave their names as members, about five and twenty.' By a strange coincidence one of the names was Thomas Birch, the same as that of our present esteemed President.

The Society's activities were to be discussions, and rambles and field meetings in summer, when papers would be read on scientific subjects relating to the locality. Subscriptions were 2s 6d.

No time was lost in fixing a ramble, for one was held in the Warren on Wednesday in Easter Week, April 15th. The Kent coal field was not yet in being, though the presence of 'blocks of coal scattered about (in the Warren) indicated that coal existed at no very great depth'. Another outing suggested was to Dungeness 'if Mr. Penn's yacht be available'. In July 1908 an excursion to Dymchurch was arranged by motor coach.

On 10th June 1868 the Committee agreed to publish *The Quarterly Journal of Folkestone Natural History Society*, the first number to be ready on 1st August. Even in those days printing could not be done as rapidly as this, and it was not ready until 1st November. Copies of this publication still exist.

At the same meeting a museum was proposed, the town possessing a valuable but much neglected collection of fossils given by Samuel J. Mackie, who wrote a history of Folkestone. The Corporation agreed to make available a room at the Sessions Hall beside the Bayle Steps in High Street, now a club. They proposed to redecorate it, but after that the Society was to name and set out the specimens, keep the room open to the public and maintain it at their own expense, no grant being offered. This was considered 'illiberal — it was regretted that the Society's proposal was received with so little sympathy', and the Secretary was requested to forward these resolutions 'hoping that the Council will be induced themselves to establish the Museum for the town on a proper footing'. The following year the Council were more co-operative and on 4th October 1870 the museum was opened by the Mayor, the foundation of our present establishment on Grace Hill. A later acquisition was the Joy Collection of butterflies.

In January 1870 the regular series of winter lectures was started. Hitherto lectures were arranged as convenient, mostly during the summer, but in the winter of 1869 there were two talks on Darwinism, a new and controversial, not to say explosive, subject. Afternoon classes were also begun in the autumn for geology and botany, prizes being offered for specimens set out and named. 'A Microscopical Conversazione, limited to members' was held on 13th May 1868. Several small conversaziones, exhibitions and minor social events were held over the years, usually in the houses of the President or committee members, but one was arranged at the Town Hall, the forerunner of our Annual Conversazione and Exhibition. It is interesting how consistently the pattern of the Society's activities has been followed down the years.

The old programmes of lectures, ranging from science, archaeology and foreign travel, show that the Society was prompt in obtaining speakers on leading scientific problems of the day; but it is a little surprising to find a paper on Television as early as 1910, and *The Atom within the Atom* given by Mr A. H. Ullyett, with experiments, in 1913. A lantern lecture on *Radio-Activity and the Structure of the Atom*, given in December 1920 by Major A. Denham DSO, MA, BSc, 'held the interest of his audience from first to last, and though some might not appreciate everything in the lecture owing to lack of preliminary training, yet all were stimulated to further reading and inquiry'.

As with most institutions, there were ups and downs; and events in 1914 were a major jolt, in spite of the detachment recorded in the minutes of the opening meeting on 29th October: 'The attendance was small compared to former years, which was fully accounted for by the prevailing unfavourable weather and by the distractions incident to the terrible war raging on the other side of the Channel'! On 14th January 1915 the minutes of the AGM record, 'During the past year the Society has pursued the even tenor of its way, which has been marked by no special feature calling for notice, except that in common with almost every other interest it has suffered from the existence of the war, which has absorbed the energies and diverted the attention of some of our members in other directions.' Joint lectures were arranged with Folkestone Camera Club; and the genius of the President, Mr G. C. Walton, kept the Society's activities going until October 1917, 'when so many of the Camera Club's members had entered the Army, and the Government's restrictions on out-of-door photographs had quite put an end to the work of the Society' not to mention dark nights and moonlight air raids 'which made it impracticable to continue the Meetings'. It was decided to adjourn, optimistically 'until some convenient date in the first fortnight of January 1918' — but there were no more Meetings until October 1919.

There were several changes of name before reverting to the original *Folkestone Natural History Society*. From 1893 to 1912 it became *Folkestone Natural History and Microscopical Society*; then *Folkestone Natural History and General Sciences Society*, retaining this until 1927. Several meeting places were used over the years. When the Sessions Hall was no longer available, the Harveian Institute on the Bayle was considered, but turned down as too dear at 2s 6d for two hours; other suggestions were a room at the Town Hall, the Bathing Establishment or the Commercial Hall. Subsequently meetings were held at the Technical Institute, and then at the Lady Sassoon Room when the Public Library was built.

In 1928 the Society celebrated its Diamond Jubilee. To mark the occasion, several meetings were held and a public lecture arranged; this was given by Professor Julian Huxley, MA, the subject being *The Progress of Biological Science during the past Sixty Years*. An address given by the District Secretary of the Kent Education Council, *The Place of Natural History in the School Curriculum*, drew attention to a serious problem, namely the decline in interest, since the turn of the century, in natural science. He deplored its neglect in schools, an unsatisfactory state of affairs that lasted until the 1939 war, and stressed its value in quickening and cultivating the faculties of observation, teaching the learner to reason from facts, 'not to mention the utility and applicability of science both in domestic and industrial life'. He concluded, 'A Society like yours should do much to keep the flag of science flying.'

During these sixty years it was remarkable that only three Presidents were in office, Dr C. E. Fitzgerald MD — 25 years; Dr S. Eastes — 12 years; and Mr G. C. Walton FLS — 23 years. He remained in office until his death in 1934 and was followed by Alderman J. Stainer JP. Longevity of service also extended to the Secretaries, as shown by these periods of office: H. Ullyett 1868–1896; Stuart Hills 1896–1908; J. Quick 1908–1911; G. W. Tuck 1911–1920; T. J. Forbes 1920–1923; J. W. Walton 1923–1948, son of Mr G. C. Walton. When natural history was in the doldrums, Mr Walton did a great deal to interest senior school boys, encouraging them to read their own papers to the Society. One of these was Raymond Casey, of Dover Road School, now Dr Raymond Casey PhD, FGS, the leading authority on fossils of SE England. Another service to the town was the setting up at the museum of living botanical specimens for eight months of the year, and still continued.

Although it was possible for some time to brush aside the 1914 war as a tactless distraction interrupting the serious work of the Society, no such grand gesture was possible in 1939. The prompt evacuation of most of the population; wholesale closing of business; the taking over of many buildings by Government departments and the forces; mining and barring with barbed wire of almost the whole English coastline, declared a prohibited area for civilians; and destruction by air raids, flying bombs, long-range shelling and sea warfare, obliged the Society to adjourn for the duration.

Strangely, during the war years there was a remarkable revival of interest in natural history, and a great demand for books on natural science and gardening. The population, returning by degrees to war-damaged towns, starved of culture for more than five years, and in a vastly more serious mood than after the Armistice in 1918, were ready to welcome the re-opening of learned societies, and Folkestone Natural History Society resumed its meetings in September 1946.

The new President was Mr A. M. Morley OBE, MA, FRES, a distinguished entomologist. The Secretary, Mr John Walton FGS,

FLS, being in poor health, introduced an innovation in nominating as Assistant Secretary Vera F. P. Day NDH, a native of Kent and a newcomer to Folkestone, who had been helping him and Mrs Walton with the wild flower exhibit at the museum. All too soon his illness became progressive, necessitating his retirement, and in 1948 the Assistant Secretary was appointed Honorary General Secretary. Mr J. Walton, as Vice-President, and a keen and competent Committee, amply camouflaged the new Secretary's inexperience in local affairs, and further help was forthcoming when Mr Morley in his wisdom appointed Miss A. J. Wright BEM, to be Assistant Secretary. An old member of the Society, and a notable Folkestone character, she was a glutton for work, and served efficiently and loyally for twelve years until her death in January 1961 at the age of 80. It was she who was responsible for reviving the Annual Conversazione. On Mr Morley's retirement in 1950, Mrs John Walton accepted the Presidency, thus following the 'Walton tradition', but her time in office was unhappily cut short in 1952 when her husband's serious condition required all her devoted attention until his death in February 1953.

Another project came the way of the Society in 1950. During the Festival of Britain, the town arranged a tattoo and exhibition of the life and work of Folkestone's trade and institutions on the cricket ground. The present Secretary, a trained gardener with some experience of staging at flower shows, felt that the Natural History Society should be represented and, accordingly, a botanical exhibit was displayed. This aroused so much interest that when the Flower Show was put on a permanent footing as a summer event, the Society were asked to contribute an exhibit. This has been staged every year since then.

For several years the lectures continued in much the same style as in former years. A great honour was an outstanding lecture in 1951 by the Astronomer Royal, Sir Harold Spencer Jones FRS. Another well-remembered occasion was when John Lester FLS, Curator of the Reptile House at the London Zoo, brought with him a live baby alligator. The startled reaction of the audience when asked to pass it round gave rise to a number of stories, progressively sensational, but the creature was actually only eighteen inches long, and very sleepy. Then a dramatic advancement in the techniques of photography and films, especially colour photography, and in new methods of slide and film projection, changed the pattern of presentation out of all recognition. Although it had been feared that the coming of television would mean the end of live lectures and entertainment, this did not happen; audiences, having come to recognize personalities like Maxwell Knight, Dr W. Swinton and Hugh Newman, were interested to meet them and hear direct about their special subjects. In some ways these new visual aids simplified the arranging of lectures, for, if in an emergency an advertised lecturer was unable to appear, some of our own members could be called upon at short notice to provide a programme of colour slides of very high quality. Several of our members have appeared on TV, in particular John Sankey BSc, FZS in a talk on badgers, and George Shannon LDS, MBOU, who has participated in a number of ornithological expeditions in several countries, and has an international reputation for bird photography.

New methods meant that the Sassoon Room was no longer adequate for our meetings, and in 1955 the President, Mr T. W. Birch MSc, MEd, the Divisional Education Officer, who had succeeded Mrs Walton in 1952, kindly arranged for us to have the use of the hall of the new Christ Church Primary School, Brockman Road. These admirable premises are comfortable and easy of access, with plenty of room for lectures and for the Annual Conversazione, hitherto held under cramped and awkward conditions at the Technical Institute, Grace Hill. Mr Birch's wide interests and great organizing ability have been of immense benefit to the Society, greatly enlarging our contacts with educational and scientific bodies, and enabling us to launch out into several projects, including an annual Nature Competition for Schools, and later, a Schools Nature Quiz. This arose out of similar brains trusts sponsored by Maxwell Knight during visits of the South Eastern Union of Scientific Societies in 1955 and 1965, at which Folkestone Natural History Society was the host. Previous visits had been in 1912 and 1925.

Two important public lectures, illustrated by colour transparencies, were arranged by the President in December 1953 and November 1958, and given to packed audiences. Both were given by George Lowe, the official photographer for Sir John Hunt's Everest expedition and Sir Vivian Fuch's trans-Antarctic expedition to the South Pole, the first at the Leas Cliff Hall, and the second, repeated twice for schools, at the Pleasure Gardens Theatre. The entire profits, amounting to about £280, were given to the Royal Geographical Society.

Since 1960, the Society's efforts have been directed towards the preservation of the countryside, threatened by the relentless demands of housing and industry, and the erection of atomic power stations and oil refineries, and, what could well be a more insidious danger, the rapid development of chemical sprays. This work has been done in co-operation with county and national bodies interested in conservation, such as the National Trust, the World Wildlife Fund, the Council for Nature, the Kent Naturalists Trust and Kent Field Club, and others. The Society was taken to task by some organizations for not opposing outright the building of Dungeness Power Station, but as this was to occupy unproductive land, and the Central Electricity Generating Board proved very co-operative in studying certain objections, and in employing a full-time bird warden, it was hoped that damage to interesting wild life would be mitigated. This has proved to be the case.

The Society's field work, continuous over the years, has been described in several publications, and useful records have been kept, especially in botany and entomology. Recently a number of manuscript lists were deposited at Maidstone Museum for safe keeping and for the use of the Kent Field Club. Besides the *Quarterly Journal* mentioned, and *Transactions* published periodically until 1959, when printing costs became prohibitive, the following printed publications have been issued:

1879: A paper on *Violets*, read by H. Ullyett BSc, at an excursion to Saltwood, of which an account was published.

1880: *Rambles of a Naturalist round Folkestone.* H. Ullyett. This includes lists of plants, birds, land and fresh-water shells, and a list of butterflies and moths based on a list by Dr H. G. Knaggs MD, 1870.

1894: *List of Flowering Plants and Ferns from the Neighbourhood of Folkestone*, revised and brought up to date. G. C. Walton FLS.

1950: *Wild Flowers and Ferns of the District round Folkestone*, compiled by John W. Walton FGS, FLS based on the work of the late G. C. Walton FLS, 1894.

1952: *Some Interesting Localities round Folkestone.* Vera F. P. Day NDH, incorporated in a popular edition of John W. Walton's List.

1931: *List of Butterflies and Moths (macro Lepidoptera) in the Neighbourhood of Folkestone.* A. M. Morley MA.

1949: *The Butterflies and Moths found in Dover and Deal District.* Bernard Embry, FRES and George H. Youden FRES.

1912: *The Flora of Folkestone and its Vicinity.* G. C. Walton FLS. Reprinted from *S.E. Naturalist and Antiquary.*

1925: *Folkestone and the Country Around*. Paper-back published by the Society for members attending the SEUSS Congress in Folkestone. 1950: *Mosses of Folkestone District*. E. C. Green BA, FLS. Reprinted from *S.E. Naturalist and Antiquary*.

At the time of the Diamond Jubilee, the *Folkestone Express* thus described the activities of the Society: 'Since the formation of the Society the members have carried out a vast amount of work to the benefit of Folkestone. By means of interesting lectures they have placed before their members, and incidentally the townspeople, a wealth of information.'

At the end of the century it may be placed on record that the Society's interests and activities are very much in line with the founders' intentions. The present constitution records that the aims and objects of the Society are to work out the natural history of the locality, to promote the study of all branches of natural history and general science, and to facilitate mutual help in such study. To this end the following activities are pursued:

1. Illustrated lectures and films are given fortnightly from October till March in Christ Church School near the Central Station. (The centenary season was very generously opened by Professor Dame Kathleen Lonsdale, FRS, DSc, President of the British Association for the Advancement of Science, with a lecture entitled 'Crystals, human and animal'.) Informal meetings of the Entomological and Botanical Sections are held monthly during the winter months.

2. Excursions and field meetings are organized during the summer months.

3. An Exhibition of scientific interest and a Conversazione are held each spring.

4. Local wild flowers and plants are exhibited throughout the greater part of the year in the Central Public Library, and annually at the local Flower Show.

5. A Natural History Competition, involving field observation, is held periodically and is open to anyone up to eighteen years of age, and Nature Quizzes for children are also organized.

6. Hand duplicated publications are issued occasionally.

All indoor Meetings are open to members on payment of a single subscription of 15s per annum, and there are no additional charges for membership of Botanical and Entomological sections.

Our hope for the future is to be able to continue to serve Folkestone and our countryside.

G. H. Hones BSc

2

The GEOLOGICAL BASIS
of the Folkestone Area

The Folkestone area is made up of a number of regions of diverse topography which can be clearly seen from the many fine vantage points on the North Downs overlooking the town.

The upper surface of this chalk plateau is gently rolling, while the south-facing edge or escarpment is cut into rounded hills. Here and there on the chalk are pockets of geologically recent beds, completely free from lime, with assemblies of acid-loving plants, and where hydrangea bear flowers of heavenly blue without special treatment.

The sheer cliffs nearer Dover reveal the great depth of the chalk strata but where the escarpment meets the coast at Folkestone, the chalk has fractured and slipped on understrata of clay, forming a second distinctive region of considerable complexity, famous to naturalists, and known as the Warren.

On any fine day the coast can be seen sweeping west and then south in a magnificent bay, without any perceptible rise of land beyond it. This is Romney Marsh, a few feet above sea-level, made up of vast areas of fertile silt and infertile gravel. The fertile land provides good grazing and deep soil for crops, but the gravel areas, part bare, part covered with natural vegetation, are as different from the Downland as chalk from cheese. Their economic wealth consists of gravel now excavated in such quantities as to leave extensive freshwater lakes. To the naturalist the Marsh is a region of great diversity, with distinctive natural fauna and flora associated especially with the foreshore, the gravel areas, and the freshwater pools.

Between the chalk escarpment and the Marsh lies a topographic-
ally much more varied lowland region of sandy limestones and clays,
and with a minor escarpment, the old coastline, running westward
from Hythe. Here are numerous ancient villages, mixed farms, and
much coppice land noted in spring for primroses, bluebells and
foxgloves.

These four main regions — the Downs, the Warren, the Marsh and
the Lowlands, each with characteristic fauna and flora — owe their
nature to the underlying rocks, and their form to geological history,
especially that concerned with uplift, bending, accretion and erosion.
The latter two are much in evidence along the coast, accretion at
Dungeness, and erosion wherever groynes, walls or concrete aprons
are expensively maintained to slow down or reverse the process.

The geology of the area, which is basic to any presentation of its
natural history, can best be understood when viewed within the
broader context of the structural pattern of south-east England.
This whole region is composed mainly of the rocks of the Secondary
era (Jurassic and Cretaceous) overlying a deep Palaeozoic platform,
but the surface geology is essentially concerned with the younger
Cretaceous rocks, a sequence of the component formations being
easily identifiable in the vicinity of Folkestone.

In essence, south-east England is structurally a major anticline, or
upfolded arch, formed during the Alpine folding with a main axis
trending from west to east, but within this broad framework there are
naturally innumerable minor features which can be most important
in a local sense. In early Tertiary times the elongated dome formed a
low island of chalk between shallower seas, in which sediment was
being deposited to become the rocks of the present-day basins of
Hampshire and London. Marine action slowly planed off the crest
to expose the older underlying rocks and the relief as we know it
today, that of an eroded core surrounded by inward facing scarps, is
a direct result of the varying powers of these different older rocks to
resist the consequent denudation, the continuous sculpturing by rain
and rivers.

The original streams followed a natural pattern, flowing to the
north and south away from the higher east–west ridge in the centre,
cutting valleys in the gently dipping chalk. Once the underlying
central beds were revealed, subsequent streams, tributary to the
main rivers, carved valleys at right angles along the more easily
eroded clays. Thus, while tributaries were eroding the clay vale along

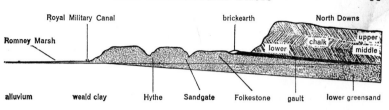

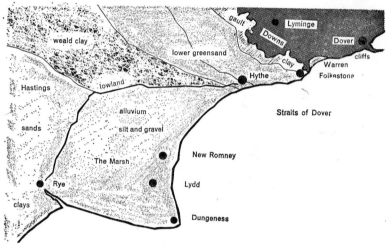

Geological Map and Section.

the foot of the scarp face of the North Downs, the main rivers were concentrating on cutting such gaps through the chalk as the Stour and Elham valleys.

Of course, the basic drainage pattern is much complicated by such other factors as changes of sea-level, river capture, the influence of the tundra conditions during the Great Ice Age, and the break-through which formed the Straits of Dover. It was this separation of Britain from the Continent which isolated the eastern end of the anticline, the chalk cliffs of France being easily visible from the Kentish coast, and created a coastline in the Folkestone area which exposed a cross-section through much of the Cretaceous system.

From west to east, a series of strata can be seen dipping in turn beneath successively younger rocks. From Lympne towards Dover, if we take the old cliff-line and temporarily turn our backs on the more recently added levels of Romney Marsh, we can see the Wealden Clay, the Lower Greensand (geologically divided into the Hythe,

Sandgate and Folkestone Beds), the bluish clay of the Gault, and finally the high cliffs of Chalk.

To the west are the coarse sands and clays of the central High Weald. Rivers, such as the Rother, flowing off these forest ridges into shallow water, assisted in the formation of the incomparably distinctive area of Romney Marsh. The old coastline can easily be traced as it marks the inner margin of the reclaimed alluvial land near Tenterden and Appledore, or around the Isle of Oxney.

Behind the long shingle ridges formed of material eroded from the cliffs of the Hastings Beds to the west of Rye, Romney Marsh has been formed both through the natural silting action of these rivers and through artificial reclamation, or 'inning', probably started in Roman times. Its present landscape is a mixture of such natural features as the beach 'fulls' of shingle (i.e. storm ridges to the west of Dungeness) and such man-made features as the large and expanding lakes resulting from shingle excavations for commercial purposes. Of course, the coastline has changed shape continuously over the years and the alignment of the truncated shingle ridges at Dungeness reflects this — so does the steady accretion of the beach on the eastern side of the point where the RNLI lifeboat station is faced with a continual problem of launching. The explanation of the sharply pointed or cuspate shape of Dungeness is generally attributed to the fact that, owing to the proximity of the French coast, no large waves reach it from the south-easterly quarter, whereas there is a large 'fetch' (distance of open water over which winds can blow and build up wave action) both to the south-west and north-east.

The long sweeping curve marking the eastern shore of Ingoldsby's 'fifth quarter of the globe' can best be seen from the vantage point by the martello tower at the western end of the Leas at Folkestone, or from the old cliff-line at Lympne, above the remains of Stutfall Castle.

Near Hythe, the blue-grey Wealden Clay, eroded throughout much of the Weald into a broad valley, disappears beneath a narrow clay belt and the first of the major Lower Greensand Beds. The sandstones of the Hythe Beds which form the hills behind the town of Hythe and as far as Seabrook, include bands of sandy limestone, known as Kentish Rag or Ragstone. Formerly extensively used as a building material — Lympne village is full of examples — it is now primarily quarried for use as road metal. Next in sequence the dark sandy clays of the Sandgate Beds continue the gentle dip to the

ERA	PERIOD	GEOLOGICAL FORMATION		ROCK TYPE OR NAME	LOCALITY
Quaternary	RECENT			Alluvium Sands & Shingle	Romney Marsh
	PLEISTOCENE			Brick-earth Clay-with-Flints	Cherry Garden Avenue Tolsford Hill
Tertiary	PLIOCENE			Lenham Beds	Dover Hill, Folkestone
	EOCENE				The Warren
65,000,000 years ago					
Secondary	UPPER CRETACEOUS	Chalk	Upper Middle Lower		North of Dover Dover Between Folkestone and Dover
		Selbornian	Upper Greensand not present Gault	Clay	Copt Point
	LOWER CRETACEOUS	Vectian	Lower Greensand	Folkestone Beds Sandgate Beds Hythe Beds	East Cliff Lower Leas Sene Valley Golf Club
		WEALDEN	Weald Clay		Behind Hythe/Palmarsh
			Hastings Beds	Sands and Clays	Fairlight Cliffs
190,000,000 years ago					
Primary		Deep Coal Measures			
Archean not present					

north-east and, after supporting Sandgate itself, appear again in much of the lower cliff face of the Leas. Small streams eroding headward from the coast have cut quite deep valleys inland across these strata and consequently break the smooth pattern of relief. Landslips, normally resulting from drainage difficulties, are frequently a problem in this area.

The town of Folkestone rests almost completely on the Folkestone Beds, rather soft, fine light brown or greenish sands, sometimes with intervening bands of calcareous sandstone and irregular seams of ferruginous carstone. These form most of the Leas Cliff face and are well exposed at East Cliff, backing the beach and promenade to the east of the harbour area, although sometimes cut by gully erosion and occasionally overlain by small fans of clay brought from the Gault which appears in the upper section of the cliff there.

These blue Gault clays dip gradually eastwards until they constitute the classic exposure of the whole cliff face at Copt Point before disappearing, in turn, beneath the chalk. The deposition of large thicknesses of mud on top of the Lower Greensand Beds, the junction being marked by a bed of phosphatic nodules, has formed a series of clay beds which are probably the most interesting and best known of all the geological formations in the area. The rich and varied fauna of the Gault sea has resulted in a wide range of easily accessible fossils, often in an excellent state of preservation. The principal fossil is the ammonite and, because of the correlation between species and strata, it is used as a reliable guide on which to base the subdivision of the Gault into zones, through the pale grey marls at the top to the very dark clays near the base.

Beyond Copt Point is the wild and scenically attractive area of very confused relief, the Warren, lying between the high Chalk cliffs of the North Downs and the sea. Here huge masses of chalk and the underlying Gault have slipped seawards with a semicircular rotatory movement about a horizontal axis, probably because marine erosion of the Gault 'toe' meant that there was insufficient support for the mass of chalk above. Inland, the Gault outcrops in a relatively narrow belt along the foot of the chalk scarp, often partially covered by material eroded from the steep slopes above.

From the scarp eastward, the chalk beds exposed along the tall cliffs between Folkestone and Dover are mostly of the Lower Series, very grey when compared with the white chalks of the Upper Series which appear in the cliffs east of Dover. These beds eventually dip as a syncline (downfold) beneath the alluvium deposited since Roman times in Wantsum Channel, before reappearing in the Isle of Thanet.

The chalk is a remarkably pure limestone and recent research suggests that, although including many types of fossil remains, it is mainly of vegetable origin, being composed of accumulations of microscopic plant life. The silica flints which occur in such prominent sands and nodules, probably accumulated in the chalk after its formation, and their relation to the pervious chalk can clearly be seen in all the cliffs.

Inland, the soft, rounded relief of the chalk countryside forms a landscape which is well known for its distinctive beauty. To have such fine scenery available naturally adds much to the area's amenities but it is probably true to say that, for most visitors, it is the coastline which is the major attraction — to geologist, geographer, biologist and holiday-maker.

The dynamic nature of landscape's ever-changing form is well portrayed on the coast. The complex interaction of natural and man-made forces can be seen in the modern design of the sea-wall backing the broad sands at Dymchurch, the massive concrete sea defences at Sandgate, and the regularly-spaced groynes intended to prevent the steady eastward longshore drift which emphasizes the resultant strength of different wave action — one result of which is the huge accumulation of shingle to the west of Folkestone Pier.

The present landscape pattern is a composite picture in which the geography of the past is continually being modified, even as we watch. The landscape, as we see it, is a palimpsest or manuscript, on which the additions of today — the new housing development, the airfield, or the caravan site — are superimposed on the patterns made during earlier phases in its history. However, the variety of the underlying physical base shows through always — not only in its effect on communications or land use, but also in all aspects of natural life.

G. H. Hones BSc

3

The GEOGRAPHICAL PATTERN of the Folkestone Area

The geography of the Folkestone area exemplifies how closely related the physical and human elements of an environment may be, with the different activities of the region reflecting the variety of the underlying physical background.

Understandably it is the geology of the area which tends to be the dominant basic influence with the topography being so much determined by the rock type and structural alignment. In addition, however, to the relief changes so apparent to the onlooker, the other components of the physical landscape also owe much of their character to the underlying geology, the inter-relationships between such elements as rock, drainage and soil being complex and highly developed.

Another element which has a major effect on the human geography of the area is the climate. The overall climate of the district owes much to its general location in the extreme south-east of the country, only separated from the continent of Europe by the Straits of Dover, and with this continental influence often far more important than the usual maritime control prevalent over most of the British Isles. The climatic variation within the district, however, is as important as these overall influences, there being quite distinct differences resulting from changes in altitude, aspect, or distance from the sea.

The physical variety within the region, and the related differences in development, enables the Folkestone district to be sub-divided into four minor regions, each of which can be studied in turn.

No one can know the North Downs without becoming aware of their distinctive qualities and these are very evident in the Folkestone area. The smooth rounded relief of the chalk hills is both attractive and striking, in the dominant scarpline at Caesar's Camp or in the wider area of the dip slope trending to the north-east, gently dissected by a system of dry valleys. Rarely is much surface water seen, except for the springline activity at the foot of the scarp so often marked by trees and shrubs, but when the water table is high enough in the chalk, the floors of erstwhile dry valleys have their 'bournes', i.e. intermittent streams, flooding the lower levels.

The higher relief of these Downs causes more cloud and precipitation than is experienced on the lower lands near by but farming in the region is generally more concerned with local variations in micro-climatology, related to shelter and aspect. Naturally the sunnier south-facing slopes are generally sought while the frost hollows, where dense cold air collects when a clear night encourages heat loss by radiation, are avoided for all such sensitive land use as fruit orchards. These orchards form only one part, even though important, of a complex land use pattern of mixed farming, bordered by the rough grazing lands offered by the steep slopes of the scarp face.

A chalk quarry breaking the line of the crest of the scarp behind Newington demonstrates the present demand for lime and this region has also played its part in helping to supply the local need for building material. One brickfield using a superficial clay deposit, has operated near Hawkinge until recently, while flints have often been utilized, as in Elham Church.

The physical environment has naturally always been very influential in the siting of settlement and the formation of the communications pattern. Both Alkham and Elham, for example, illustrate the importance of shelter, available water supply, and control of a valley route. However, geographical values are in a continual state of change and this is emphasized by the little evidence that remains of the old Elham Valley railway line, while caravans now congregate in exposed positions on the cliffs at Capel, in order to be near the main road and gain a Channel view! Below these chalk cliffs, other holiday-makers are attracted to a new camping site in the Folkestone Warren, the second of the local regions.

The Warren's distinctive qualities are derived directly from the complex geology and relief that result from its history of major landslips. Irregular in relief and drainage, it has remained isolated and somewhat inaccessible, a region of great interest to all naturalists particularly.

Apart from the recent development of the camping site at the more accessible western end, the only real penetration has been by the railway. Not only has the main link between Folkestone and Dover faced the continual threat of landslips — again in 1967 large cliff falls blocked the line on different occasions — but erosion by the sea has necessitated the building of a large concrete platform, or apron, intended to act as a sea defence as well as stabilizing the Gault clay, preventing its extrusion under the weight of the over-lying chalk.

The Gault, with springs emerging over it at Holywell by Sugarloaf Hill, and at the Cherry Garden reservoirs, marks the limit of the next region, the dissected lowland composed mainly of the Lower Greensand Beds.

As already noted, the geological variety in this region not only influence the relief and drainage but has also had a major effect on many aspects of the human geography. As would be expected the area's mineral development is a clear reflection of the pattern, and ranges widely in type and location. Brick-making was for long an important local industry using the Brick-earth deposits on the Gault, while sands are still dug in many pits today. The well-known Kentish Ragstone, a limestone of the Lower Greensand Hythe Beds, has been used extensively in the region for building purposes and the evidence remains in many old houses, often, as at Lympne, with the supplying near-by quarries now abandoned and overgrown.

The land-use of the area is essentially mixed farming, the actual type practised being influenced by such local factors as soil, slope and drainage. The physical variety available in a short distance has long been appreciated and this is seen in the way in which farms, as well as parishes, often traverse across the geological alignment to include a maximum range of types. Agriculture, however, is gradually being forced to retreat as other demands on the land increase. Large areas have long been occupied by the War Department, as at Shorn-cliffe Camp between Cheriton and Sandgate, and the increasing need for housing has resulted in a great deal of post-war development. With land values changing, even such areas as the valley just east of Shorncliffe Camp, for long regarded as too costly to develop because of relief and drainage problems but now re-named the *Golden Valley*, are now lost to the farmer as new residential estates are created, using modern techniques to overcome the physical difficulties.

Changes in the land-use pattern have also helped to create a very different landscape in the last of the four regions, Romney Marsh. Flat and exposed, this most distinctive of regions has always had a character of its own, derived largely from its relative isolation from the rest of Kent and Sussex.

However, as improved communications of all kinds, from trunk roads to television, have reduced the earlier sense of remoteness on the Marsh, so has the cultural landscape become modified. Although one can still see the traditional Marsh farming scene with thousands of sheep grazing on lush fattening pastures between miles of winding drainage dykes, a new landscape has been superimposed in places. Straightened dykes lower the water table more efficiently, assisting the intensive cultivation of flowers and vegetables on farms with improved roads and large greenhouses alongside modern buildings.

Another major change in the region has resulted from the increased impact of tourism but, so far, the holiday camps, car parks and caravans have concentrated in a narrow coastal belt within easy access of the beaches. The busy summer activity by the sea-wall provides a remarkable contrast with the quiet rural scene only a mile or two inland.

A much closer juxtaposition of the old and new landscapes is seen at Dungeness Point where the immense nuclear power stations tower over the cottages of the small fishing community and the well-known Nature Reserve. This scene is symptomatic of the problems facing our coastal areas to-day and the need for careful intelligent planning if we are to maintain the geographical values of the past while permitting changes to aim at the future.

Vera F. P. Day NDH & K. Dilys Rowlands BA

4

PLANT RESPONSE
in the District

For botanical purposes, the Folkestone district can be divided into five distinct regions, most nearly associated with the underlying geological features and the resultant topography. Patches of a particular soil may give rise to an entirely different type of vegetation within a region, such as that of acid clay in the Hougham area, unlike anything nearer than Tunbridge Wells. For convenience these regions can be described as follows:

1. The Chalk Downs and their valleys.
2. The large and varied country between the Downs and the coast, of clay, greensand, and Kentish rag.
3. Romney Marsh, reclaimed agricultural land with its dykes, and stretches of shingle bordering the sea.
4. The Warren, a medley of soils deposited by landslips.
5. The sea coast, with its outstanding white cliffs, sands and shingle beds.

THE CHALK DOWNS AND THEIR VALLEYS

The rounded hills, long sweeping lines and abrupt escarpments, with dazzling patches of bare chalk, form the outstanding features of the Downs. Lying in their folds are small dry valleys or coombs, their sides often covered with scrub consisting of wayfaring tree *Viburnum lantana*, spindle *Euonymus europaeus*, dogwood *Cornus sanguinea*, privet *Ligustrum vulgare*, traveller's joy *Clematis vitalba*, hawthorn *Crataegus monogyna*, and sweet briar *Rosa rubiginosa*. The larger valleys, also waterless except when the nailbournes are flowing, support beech woods and their scanty ground flora of mosses, and in places butterfly orchids *Platantera chlorantha* and *P. bifolia*, and several helleborines *Epipactis* and *Cephalanthera*. Beech trees are capable of growing to a large size on very shallow soil, and woods apparently perched precariously on steep hillsides are called hangers.

Small streams cutting through the chalk have carved out long narrow valleys, usually well wooded. One such typical chalk valley, at Denton, is described elsewhere.

The chalk has a very diverse flora, largely of small wiry-stemmed plants with bright-coloured flowers, outstanding species being wild thyme, rock rose, milkwort, horseshoe vetch, centaury, yellow wort, squinancy wort, carline and ground thistles, autumn gentian, lady's bedstraw, marjoram, scabious, large knapweed, creeping rest-harrow and quaking grass, with a large number of orchids (bee, scented, pyramidal, man and lady's tresses). Wherever the chalk is freshly exposed, tall species will spring up; viper's bugloss, dyer's rocket or weld, wild mignonette, great mullein with large woolly leaves, red valerian and musk thistle.

Although at first sight the chalk country appears to follow an overall pattern very closely, there are distinct differences. The striking round-headed rampion, common on the Sussex Downs, is absent in Kent, while the late spider orchid *Ophrys aranifera* is confined to East Kent. The valleys also have their characteristic variations. Sweet briar is plentiful in the Elham Valley, with nettle-leaved bellflower *Campanula trachelium* and stinking iris *Iris foetidissima*, and strange fungi in the woods, where orpine *Sedum telephium* and twayblade *Listera ovata* are plentiful. Musk orchid *Herminium monorchis* and the rare *Corydalis bulbosa* are to be found. White poplar is conspicuous on the hill slopes of the Alkham Valley, with white melilot *Melilotus alba*, sainfoin *Onobrychis viciifolia* and moon daisies along the roadsides. In the woods along the valley bottoms are woodland hawthorn *Crataegus oxycanthus* and many handsome ferns. Around Lyminge the woods bordering the steep-sided road cuttings are on clay-with-flints, with neutral vegetation, green hellebore *Helleborus viridis*, herb paris *Paris quadrifolia*, woodruff *Asperula odorata*, goldilocks *Ranunculus auricomus*, red currant *Ribes rubrum*, ramsons *Allium ursinum*, and toothwort *Lathraea squamaria* parasitic on hazel.

The Lynsore Valley, of chalk with clay-with-flints, is still more varied. Chalk flora abounds, with cowslips and hairy violets *Viola hirta* and very many orchids on chalky banks, including the man *Aceras anthropophorum* and fly *Ophrys insectifera*, and in the woods the beautiful lady orchid *Orchis purpurea*. Here is whitebeam *Sorbus aria*, not common in the district, with elder and yew; and at the edge of the woods, along the road verges, cow wheat *Melampyrum sylvaticum*, wall lettuce *Mycelis muralis*, and the pretty wood melick grass *Melica uniflora*. On the opposite side of the valley the woods are damper, and here is guelder rose *Viburnum opulus*, some lady orchids, but more butterfly orchids, and several broomrapes including the rare blue broomrape *Orobanche caerulea*. Along the woodland paths are wood vetch *Vicia sylvatica*, tuberous bitter vetch *Lathyrus macrorrhizus*, orpine and yellow nettle *Galeobdolon lutea*, and the beautiful uncommon wood millet grass *Milium effusum*, tall and very pale green.

The Forestry Commission has planted up large areas in these valleys, and several nature reserves have been established.

Further inland the country is quite different. From the chalk valleys beyond Lyminge the land rises to a more or less level elevated plateau traversed by the Roman Stone Street. From Lyminge to Stelling Minnis it is largely forest country, the soil being sandy and native trees are silver birch, willows, and aspen *Populus tremulus*, but the plantations are mainly of conifers. In places the soil is acid. Hard fern *Blechnum spicant* is common and there are small patches of ling in the woodland rides. There was formerly a good deal on the common at Stelling Minnis, but it has been driven out by bracken. On neutral areas in the woods are lilies of the valley, and in damp sites an abundance of wild angelica *Angelica sylvestris*. There are wild raspberries in these woods, and on Stelling Minnis.

Beyond Stelling Minnis the soil is heavier, a clay loam, indicated by wild crab trees, and many grasses along the road verges. This is good agricultural land, with fruit-growing and several market gardens as well as farm crops. The attractive chicory *Chicorium intybus* indicates where the chalk begins again. Even where it is thin, the soil in the chalk valleys is good, and on the lower slopes where it is deep, agriculture is varied. Weeds of cultivation are scentless mayweed, annual spurges, fumitory, pennycress *Thlaspi arvensis*, white goosefoot *Chenopodium album*, charlock and lesser broomrape *Orobanche minor*, a pest in clover fields. Some years there will spring up the strange thorn apple *Datura stramonium*, one of the poisonous *Solanaceae*, but usually avoided by cattle. The true deadly nightshade *Atropa belladonna*, a small shrub with large black berries, is another native of the chalk.

These brief notes can only give some impression of the beauty and richness of the local flora, and its remarkable range of species.

FROM DOWNS TO COAST

Southwards, between the chalk hills and the coast, the landscape is wide and varied. At the foot of the Downs lies a clay belt which ends in the Warren, at East Wear Bay. This stretch of lowland, often referred to as the Vale of Holmesdale, is mainly farm land, occupied by pasture and fodder crops, with woods of oak, ash and hazel periodically coppiced for fencing, bean poles, and hurdles. The ground flora is considerable, and typical of woods where the shade is not dense — bluebells, primroses, often in bloom before Christmas, violets, wood anemones, early purple orchids and bugle. Along damp shaded road verges are spotted orchids *Dactylorchis fuchsii*, lady's smock *Cardamine pratensis*, and great pendulous sedge *Carex pendula*. Weeds of cultivation are mainly wild radish *Raphanus sativus*, annual mercury *Mercurialis annua*, redshank or persicaria *Polygonum persicaria*, charlock *Sinapis arvensis*, and several of the *Chenopodiaceae*, all characteristic of alkaline clay soils. There are many species of grasses including the woodland brome *Bromus ramosus*, and among the grass will be found the grass vetchling *Lathyrus nissolia* and the uncommon narrow-leaved form of the common vetch with crimson flowers *Vicia sativa* sp. *angustifolia*. At Ashford the Vale of Holmesdale joins the brick-earth of the orchard country, and beyond Aldington it merges into the high ground of the Weald by way of the Greensand ridge dividing it from Romney Marsh.

The Greensand rocks, of sandstones and clays, begin at Copt Point, and an abrupt break occurs where the little river Foord has cut a deep ravine between East Cliff and the Leas before entering the sea at Folkestone Harbour. Outcrops of clay in several places, notably on East Cliff, Dover Hill, Sandgate Hill and Lower Sandgate Road are indicated by dense growth of fragrant butterbur *Petasites fragrans*. A wide bank of shingle covering the site of the Roman stone quarry separates the sea from the wooded cliffs of the Leas, and no shore vegetation is present except a few patches of sea blite *Suaeda maritima*, sea purslane *Halimione portulacoides* and sea beet *Beta maritima*. The first two are salt marsh plants but surprisingly grow on dry retaining walls of the shrubbery bordering the promenade.

Pine trees and masses of blackthorn with some evergreen oaks *Quercus ilex*, cover the cliffs; ground flora includes wild wallflowers, stinking iris and alexanders *Smyrnium olusatrum*. Many shrubs have been planted by the Corporation, usually in mown grass, which keeps down most plants except celandines. Where the trees thin out at the toll-gate chalk plants occur, together with alkaline sandy species which grow abundantly along the banks on the Leas. Prominent among these are valerian *Centranthus ruber*, sea pink or thrift *Armeria maritima*, strong smelling lettuce *Lactuca virosa*, crow garlic *Allium vineale*, corn salad or lamb's lettuce *Valerianella locusta*, stonecrops *Sedum acre, S. album*, and *S. dasyphyllum*, the minute early forget-me-not *Myosotis collina*, stork's-bill *Erodium cicutarium*, creeping rest-harrow *Ononis repens*, spotted medick *Medicago arabicum*, a number of clovers, including haresfoot, rough, soft knotted and subterranean, also a rare small grass *Poa bulbosa*. An unusual dark red continental scabious *Scabiosa atropurpurea* grows in quantity along the Leas from the bandstand down the Road of Remembrance. Where clay comes to the surface on the cliffs the ground is covered with the pernicious Thanet weed or curse-of-Kent *Cardaria draba*. At midsummer golden scented pyramids of field cabbage *Brassica arvensis* are very attractive.

Springs and small streams are characteristic of the Greensand. They are usually free flowing and very shallow, with vegetation that roots in mud and gravel, mainly booklime *Veronica beccabunga*, water pepper *Polygonum hydropiper*, watercress *Nasturtium officinalis*, and procumbent marsh wort *Apium nodosum*. In a little stream below the Leas Cliff Hall can be found the uncommon brookweed *Samolus valerandi*, which likes running streams near the sea.

A large area of neutral sandy soil stretches across country from Cherry Garden Lane through Shorncliffe to Saltwood, in places sufficiently acid to allow lime-hating garden plants to be grown while in the woods are many beautiful ferns, and a few wild daffodils. Round about Saltwood, alder carrs occupy the damp valley bottoms, where marsh marigold *Caltha palustris* and golden saxifrage *Saxifraga oppositifolium* grow. Crack willow *Salix fragilis* and field maple *Acer campestris* are common, and the old railway line and adjoining woods have been colonized by the salmonberry, a crimson-flowered raspberry from Canada *Rubus spectabilis*, which appeared on a Canadian camping site near Shorncliffe after the 1914 war and has spread steadily. Another uncommon plant in the woods is the blue and yellow forget-me-not *Myosotis discolor*. But the predominating flower of late spring is the pink campion *Lychnis dioica*. Weeds of cultivation are characteristic of light soils; wild pansy *Viola tricolor*, spurrey

Spergula arvensis, many-seeded goosefoot *Chenopodium polyspermum*, corn marigold *Chrysanthemum segetum*, and black nightshade *Solanum nigrum*. Occasionally the poisonous henbane *Hyoscyamus niger* will appear, and disappear again for long periods.

Behind the canal bank at Hythe is an escarpment of Kentish rag, which has the character of limestone. Several limestone plants occur here, hound's tongue *Cynoglossum officinale*, milk thistle *Silybum marianum*, danewort *Sambucus ebulus* and the large pink bindweed *Calystegia sylvatica*. In many places a sage *Salvia sclarea* with dark blue flowers is plentiful, and a number of stone walls are covered in spring with the tiny whitlow grass *Eriophila verna* which is a flowering plant, and a genuine small grass with stiff reddish flattened heads, mat grass *Nardus stricta*.

ROMNEY MARSH

For centuries the Marsh has been pasture land, carrying more sheep to the acre than anywhere else in the kingdom. Although the Marsh is described elsewhere, certain details of the flora are worth recording.

The soil, formed from the washdown of the Wealden clay and the weathering of the greensand ridge, is a deep, rather heavy calcareous loam. Apart from weeds of cultivation, most species grow mainly in and along the ditches and dykes, and on their banks, and consist of water-loving plants that prefer an alkaline medium. Hence, in the inland dykes will be found the sub-species of water crowfoot *Ranunculus aquatilis*, *R. a. circinatus* and *R. a. peltatus*, sub-species *pseudo fluitans*, a calcareous plant. Three species of water sweet grass *Glyceria* and fox sedge *Carex vulpina*, are fairly widespread. Where the soil is lighter can be found the two reed maces *Typha latifolia* and *T. angustifolia*, and the lovely flowering rush *Butomus umbellatus*, with the uncommon great water parsnip *Sium latifolium*. A newcomer to the Marsh in recent years is the lesser bladderwort *Urtricularia minor*. As might be expected, several species of willow occur inland, usually along the roadside ditches. Pepper saxifrage *Silaum silaus* grows in the grass verges, with wild carrot *Daucus carota*.

The tall handsome reed *Phragmites communis* is abundant throughout the Marsh, with the attractive reed-grass *Phalaris arundinacea*. Several species of water dropwort (*Oenanthe*) grow equally well in fresh and brackish conditions.

In some years during early spring the inland dykes are red with a tiny water plant *Azola filiculoides* floating on the surface, while the

3

brackish dykes are yellow green with the curling tubes of a floating laver *Ulva intestinalis.*

Dykes near the coast contain brackish water and the vegetation differs somewhat from that of the inland waterways. Characteristic of brackish water are the water crowfoot species *R. a. baudotii* and *R. a. spaerospermus,* the seaside rush *Juncus acutus,* the sea club rush *Scirpus montanus,* and the seaside sedge *Scirpus tabernae-montani,* and salt meadow sedge *Carex divisa.* In one place there is a considerable amount of the rare Borrer's salt marsh grass *Puccinellia fasciculata.* Typical of the coastal dykes is the beautiful marsh mallow *Althaea officinalis.* A salt marsh plant, the strong smelling wild celery *Apium graveolens,* has invaded the dykes in places, but strangely in dry weather it will make its way up the banks into the shelter of the blackthorn hedges. Along the road verges are wild parsnip *Pastinacea sativa* and teasel *Dipsacus fullonum* in abundance, both calcareous plants. A particularly noticeable weed of cultivation, along the edges of arable land, is the tall handsome corn sowthistle *Sonchus arvensis* with olive green buds and large orange yellow flowers.

From Hythe to New Romney the coast road passes between the Marsh proper on the one hand, and on the other the large stretches of shingle that divide the Marsh from the sea, except where the road runs directly under the sea-wall between the Redoubt and Dymchurch. A small canal bounds the front gardens of houses adjoining the road past the Beach Holiday Camp. In spring an impressive sight in this part of the Marsh is the multitude of flowering hawthorns, planted specially down the years to provide faggots for consolidating Dymchurch wall, originally built of mud, and now of stone and concrete.

Much of the shingle area is used by the War Department as a training ground and firing range, and in the last few years has been fenced so that access is no longer possible. A great deal of the shingle is deep, loose and bare of vegetation, but much of it is sufficiently consolidated to support a peculiar flora. There is much gorse, but the principal shrub is the curious prostrate blackthorn laden with sloes in the autumn, the fruiting branches lying along the ground. This habit is perhaps induced by the windswept site, as may be the case with the curious prostrate broom of Dungeness, but small upright trees do occur as well; and there is much else of botanical interest in this arid landscape. Where the shingle is loose, but shallow and fairly stable, there spring up between the stones in the early part of the year thousands of tiny ephemerals, which dry up and disappear in summer. Colour of flowers and leaves is often intensified, doubtless by the extra heat reflected from the stones, and from the intense light.

Along the road verges where there is some depth of soil, taller plants make a brilliant border throughout the summer, apparent even to motorists passing through. The most attractive are viper's bugloss, red valerian, wild parsnip and wild carrot, sand leek *Allium scorodoprasum*, bladder campion, opium poppies, great mullein, several thistles, lady's bedstraw, a white bedstraw *Galium erectum*, toad flax *Linaria vulgaris*, and lasting well into November, ragwort and some handsome red docks.

At New Romney the road turns inland, and the shingle widens out into the Lydd ranges and the land now occupied by Lydd Airport. Some of this is rough grazing for sheep, which gradually gives way to bare shingle again that eventually merges into the grim windswept reaches of Dungeness.

In recent years excavations for gravel are changing the landscape in places by creating small lakes and depositing small mounds that soon become colonized by wild plants, some being of continental origin, like the eastern rocket *Sisymbrium orientale*, tumbling mustard *Sisymbrium altissimum*, and italian toadflax *Linaria purpurea*.

THE WARREN

At the foot of the chalk cliffs between Dover and Folkestone lies the Warren, a broken landscape of chalk hummocks, weathered greensand, deposits of red iron-bearing sands of the Lenham Beds spilled over the cliff tops, and mounds and slopes of adhesive slippery blue gault, piled up or scattered around in the confusion of successive landslips. At the foot of Dover Hill the gault comes to the surface. Springs have washed away the thin covering of top soil, and keep the gault in a wet condition and constantly on the move. The weight of the chalk cliffs squeezes it out at the shore, where wave action disintegrates it and causes cliff falls.

All these soil types carry their own particular vegetation, so that the Warren is of great interest to naturalists. Further samples of soils, dumped by the Corporation in an attempt to check erosion, have added seedlings of garden plants and alien weeds; canary grass *Phalaris canariensis*, Oxford ragwort *Senecio squalidus*, the attractive red goosefoot *Chenopodium rubrum*, safflower *Carthamnus tinctorius*, and in particular the common buddleia *Buddleia davidii*.

A short distance below the Roman site is a large outcrop of gault prevented from further slipping across the beach by a bank of green-sand on which grow sallow and eared willow *Salix aurita*, blackthorn and sea buckthorn *Hippophae rhamnoides*. When the gault is held up small ponds form, usually scummy with blanket weed, but some-times clear enough for the small-flowered water crowfoot *R. a. drouetti* to establish itself until the next landslide buries it and temporarily wipes out the ponds. The striking great water horsetail *Equisetum telmatei* grows all down the slope, with codlins-and-cream willow herb, mud horsetail *Equisetum limosum*, common rush and its variants, and a small amount of water mint. The drier parts of these slopes are covered with coarse tor grass, tufted sedge *Carex elata*, wild carrot, coltsfoot, melilot, and some brambles, with welted and slender-flowered thistle, and prickly lettuce *Lactuca serriola*. Teasels are plentiful, and milkwort survives under black bent grass.

Above the lower promenade at East Cliff attempts to stabilize the cliffs by planting have proved ineffective, as the plants' roots turn away from the impenetrable plastic mass, and a shrub will form a mat of roots on the surface, in time sliding under its own weight.

At the foot and on the slopes of the chalk cliffs in Little Switzer-land, gay little chalk flowers once flourished in profusion, but the smothering tor grass and hemp agrimony growing up in the absence of rabbits, and the establishment of a caravan site, have destroyed many. They still survive, however, on the broken hummocks over-looking the railway. Where the soil is slightly deeper, gromwell *Lithospermum officinale*, wood spurge, bladder campion, and small and devil's bit scabious occur. The early spider orchid *Ophrys sphegodes* sometimes grows here, and clumps of Nottingham catchfly *Silene nutans* and the rare pink and white moth mullein *Verbascum blattaria*, to disappear for long periods. Near the martello tower horned poppy *Glaucium flavum* grows on the cliff top with clove-scented broomrape *Orobanche caryophyllaceae*, native to this part of Kent. The tall poisonous hemlock *Conium maculatum* occurs in considerable quantity.

Steep paths go down from Little Switzerland to a stretch of tumbled chalk and patches of sand, on which when newly fallen, masses of mauve opium poppy spring up. This low-lying part is covered with typical chalk scrub and brambles, with some sizeable elders and field maples. Particularly conspicuous are the fine bushes of wayfaring tree, and of recent years, an attractive red-leaved dog-wood. Underneath the scrub are quantities of the lime-loving hart's tongue fern, with stinking iris, nettle-leaved bellflower, and in damp open places, spotted orchids.

Here and there are small open stretches of grass once larger and more numerous, with little chalk plants among the grass, and near the railway line sandy patches where two white stonecrops grow, with blue fleabane *Erigeron acre*. A rare sea radish *Raphanus rugosus* grows on the railway bank, and up on the Old Dover Road. Although close to the shore, there is little invasion of sea plants, other than the wild sea cabbage which grows all over the cliffs.

Because of the underlying gault and the water absorbing quality of chalk, wild flowers can be found here and elsewhere in the chalk country in the hottest driest weather, when the rest of the countryside is parched and brown.

THE SEA COAST

North-east of Folkestone the Downs slope towards the South Fore-land and the Dover cliffs, traditionally white there but almost grey nearer Folkestone. At the foot of the cliffs on the shore, sand gives way to shingle and broken chalk. The greater sea spurrey *Spergularia media*, grows in damp pockets near white stone-crop *Sedum album*; wall-pepper *Sedum acre* is frequently seen, and sea pearlwort *Sagina maritima*; none of these a whit less pleasing that the magnificent yellow-horned poppy *Glaucium flavum*. Rock sea-lavender *Limonium binervosum*, the species that grows on cliffs, is found there and through-out, as is buck's horn plantain *Plantago coronopus*.

Flowers of the downland enliven the cliff tops, against a quiet background of alexanders and fennel *Foeniculum vulgare*. On the rifle range, the green-veined orchid *Orchis morio* is established. Early spider orchids are scattered along the cliffs and, most unexpectedly, man orchids *Aceras anthropophorum* have been growing in grass at the foot of Shakespeare cliff. The Lizard Orchid is not found nearer than Sandwich. Near Dover the burnt-tipped orchid *Orchis ustulata*, a dwarf replica of Kent's lady orchid, is followed later by autumn lady's tresses *Spiranthes spiralis*, with their dainty spiral flower spikes, and there is also a spreading colony of cypress spurge *Euphorbia cyparissias*. Sea carrot *Daucus carota*, plentiful itself, is occasionally host to a rare broomrape, *Orobanche maritima*; and hawkweed ox-tongue *Picris hieracioides*, host to another, *Orobanche picridis*. An eyebright of cliffs, *Euphrasia occidentalis*, can be seen and the chalk bedstraw *Galium pumilum*. A prostrate, woody plant, rockspray

Cotoneaster microphyllis persists, and also small bushes of the prostrate form of common juniper *Juniperus communis*, which remain small and do not seem to flower.

Further on, near the path to the Royal Oak, is a patch of golden samphire *Inula crithmoides*, a coastal plant not seen again nearer than North Kent. There is an interesting pocket of typical vegetation at Lydden Spout. Sea kale *Crambe maritima*, is on the shingle; annual seablite *Suaeda maritima*, in wet patches, and tree mallow *Lavatera arborea*, amongst grass; all to be seen, also, near Shakespeare Cliff. Higher up are sea stock *Matthiola sinuata* and wild cabbage *Brassica oleracea*, at its best above Dover, its leaves still sometimes eaten when cooked thoroughly. Rock samphire *Crithmum maritimum* also grows along the length of the cliff and has been picked for the table since the time of King Lear. Lastly, though first to flower, is the gay, fragrant wallflower *Cheiranthus cheiri*. Wild madder *Rubia peregrina* is less often seen but recurs above a near-by railway cutting. The dye was extracted from roots of this and a similar plant. It is doubtful whether clove-scented broomrape, *Orobanche caryophyllacea*, on its bedstraw host, still survives at Lydden Spout, nor has the tiny and exquisite sea heath *Frankenia laevis*, been seen there recently.

The Warren is damp, thicketed above, almost marshy below. This terrain drops down to sandy beach where saltwort *Salsola kali*, frosted orache *Atriplex laciniata*, and Babington's orache *Atriplex glabriuscula*, grow with better-known plants, common and halberd-leaved orache *A. patula* and *A. hastata*; sea sandwort *Honkenya peploides*, and sea beet *Beta vulgaris* ssp. *maritima*. Like most sea plants, these are characteristically fleshy, as are the leaves of the maritime form of scentless mayweed *Tripleurospermum maritimum* var. *salimum*, the decumbent form usual by the sea in the south. Rest-harrow *Ononis repens* is there, and nearer Copt Point, spiny rest-harrow *Ononis spinosa*.

South-west of Folkestone the beaches show little vegetation between the sea and embankments, but tree mallow, sea sandwort and sea kale still grow on an undisturbed piece of shore at Sandgate. Early scurvy-grass *Cochlearia danica* makes a pale lilac carpet under tamarisk *Tamarix gallica* at Hythe. Most of the stretch of shingle round the rifle range is now enclosed. Thrift *Armeria maritima* and yellow stonecrop *Sedum reflexum* are still there and, it is hoped, chidling pink *Kohlrauschia prolifera*. From the Redoubt to Dymchurch, sand and shingle beaches, enclosed by embankments, allow for little coastal vegetation. It is not until south of Dymchurch that sandy turf on the land side of the sea-wall gives growing room to fascinating tiny plants, many of them spring ephemerals. These can also be found elsewhere on stabilized shingle. It is worth looking at them closely. Amongst them are common whitlow grass *Erophila verna*, growing in one spot with *Erophila spathulata*; two of the smaller mouse-ear chickweeds, *Cerastium atrovirens*, usually with four petals and four sepals, and *Cerastium semidecandrum*, with five; *Moenchia erecta*, like a small stitchwort, only opening in sunshine and therefore difficult to find; thyme-leaved sandwort *Arenaria serpyllifolia*, common throughout; several stonecrops, including *Sedum anglicum*, and spring vetch *Vicia lathyroides*; fingered saxifrage *Saxifraga tridactylites*, the only true saxifrage on this coast, and two forget-me-nots, early and changing *Myosotis ramosissima*, and *M. discolor*. Two rarer plants are sand catchfly *Silene conica* at St Mary's Bay and shepherd's cress *Teesdalia nudicaulis* at Dungeness.

Little grasses to be seen are small hair-grass *Aira praecox*, bulbous meadow-grass *Poa bulbosa*, sand cat's-tail *Phleum arenarium*; and the two stiff fern-like grasses, fern grass *Catapodium rigidum* and stiff sand-grass *Catapodium marinum*, are both often found along the coast. The bearded pinkish *Vulpia ambigua*, can be conspicuous.

Other typical plants are sea campion *Silene maritima*, red-seeded dandelion *Taraxacum laevigatum*, *Stellaria pallida*, paler and less robust than the common chickweed, and amongst the clovers, rough clover *Trifolium scabrum*, soft clover *T. striatum*, and burrowing clover *T. subterraneum*, whose pods burrow into the ground. The sandy soil suits dove's-foot crane's-bill *Geranium molle* and the stork's-bill *Erodium cicutarium* ssp. *dunense*, found on dunes. On the beach at Littlestone is the smaller and stickier stork's-bill *Erodium glutinosum*, and sea rocket *Cakile maritima*. Where there are low dunes are sand sedge *Carex arenaria* and evening primroses, amongst them fragrant *Oeonthera stricta*; marram grass *Ammophila arenaria*, sand couch *Agropyron junceiforme*, and sea convolvulus *Calystegia soldanella*.

It can only be hoped that the cliffs to the north and this shingle plain to the south will be allowed to keep what is left of their natural inheritance.

A. M. Morley OBE, MA, FRES

5

MOTHS and BUTTERFLIES
of South East Kent

Of all the counties of Great Britain and Ireland it is probable that none could claim to have on record a greater range of butterflies and moths than Kent. The county has many good reasons to justify such a claim. It is of considerable size and has a very long coastline. It has a very varied terrain, composed of quaternary deposits of soil above vast layers of chalk, gault, sand, and heavy weald clay, bordered in places near the sea by areas of alluvial soil, marshland, beach sand, or, at Dungeness, coarse shingle. Such a variety of terrain produces a corresponding variety of vegetation, which in its turn nourishes very many species of lepidoptera whether as adults or as caterpillars. Kent also has a climate not unlike that of the nearest part of Europe, separated only by a narrow channel which can be crossed by the stronger fliers with ease and by the weaker with the assistance of a favourable wind.

The southern triangle of Kent has been known to entomologists for at least one hundred and forty years, though this statement applies only to the coastal area from Sandwich to the Folkestone Warren. Before 1842 Folkestone itself was little more than a village, and it was probably not until 1856 that it became well known to entomologists when some surprising discoveries were made there, and soon afterwards in the Warren. Romney Marsh was probably known to few before 1928 though Dungeness was probably known to a small secretive group before then. It was there in 1879 that Sydney Webb discovered the first British example of Webb's wainscot *Nonagria sparganii* Esp. and took care not to reveal the locality. Several entomologists collected there in 1930 and 1931, but it was not until 1934 that the remarkable captures made by Mr Lee and Sir Beckwith Whitehouse made this one of the most popular collecting grounds in the country.

The famous woods at Ham Street were practically unknown when, in 1928 or 1929, the late Col E. Scott and I made their acquaintance quite independently. Since then the Forestry Commission has altered their character in some ways, but even lately I have heard entomologists refer to them as the best woods in England.

In 1936 Dr Scott published the first list of macro-lepidoptera occurring in the neighbourhood of Ashford, Kent, covering an area of two hundred square miles within a radius of eight miles from the centre of the town. This area includes, on one side, the woods of the Weald and of Ham Street, and on the other side some of the best collecting grounds of the North Downs, about which Col C. A. W. Duffield was able to provide much valuable information. The total number of species listed in Dr Scott's book was 462, a high proportion of the then recorded species of the whole of the British Isles, which at that time probably amounted to no more than 900 macro-lepidoptera. He might have enlarged his list if he had included species recorded before 1918, but he preferred to ignore what he regarded as past history.

Fourteen years later he published the second edition of his list which now included exactly 500 species, representing an increase which more than equalled the increase in the total number of British species. Finally, while he was still Honorary Secretary of our section, he set to work on a third edition and with very great courage completed it in September 1963, in spite of a serious illness which resulted in his sudden and much lamented death. He did not live to see his book in its final form, for it was not published until 1964, by the Kent Field Club. The final edition of his work contains notes on 585 species of macro-lepidoptera, a big increase on the preceding list. In it Dr Scott has taken the bold step of adding notes on the pyrales, which some authorities include among the macro-lepidoptera, and the micro-lepidoptera, among which are now included some large or even very large moths. Of these two groups he has listed 668 species, which means that the total number of species he mentions is more than half of the 2,404 named in the well-known check-list of British Lepidoptera by I. R. P. Helsop.

In the introduction to his book Dr Scott says: 'The micro-lepidoptera are admittedly incomplete. This is largely new ground and a start had to be made. There is much scope in this respect for the improvements and additions of others, for publication as supplements from time to time.'

In 1949 the late Bernard Embry, brother of the famous airman, and G. H. Youden published the first complete list of the macro-lepidoptera occurring in the Dover, Deal and Sandwich area. This work has an excellent introduction, and the names of 596 species dealt with are accompanied by valuable notes. The area under review consists of the three towns already mentioned, the coastal district in which they are situated, a hinterland of chalk downs, and a fair number of woods. It does not, however, amount to more than one hundred and thirty square miles. For so small an area the number of species recorded is most impressive, especially as no fewer than 508 of these had been noted from 1930 to 1949. It might be added that the main list is followed by a supplementary list of 136 pyrales.

Shortly after the foundation of our Society there appeared in Simpson's *Guide to Folkestone* what seems to be the first full list of the lepidoptera of Folkestone and district to be published. It was drawn up by H. Ullyett, for many years the Honorary Secretary of our Society, and contains the names, with all too short notes, of 290 species of macro-lepidoptera. The fact that it mentions a moth which is thought not to have occurred in this country before 1869, and that the list is so much shorter than the next to be considered, suggests that it was published before the latter part of 1870.

In 1870 the Folkestone Natural History Society published a list that might well serve as a model for all future lists. It was drawn up by Dr H. Guard Knaggs, an editor of the *Entomologist's Monthly Magazine* and author of several books on entomology. The list is full of interest and the first part of the introduction is well worth quoting for its Victorian exuberance. 'As might be expected from the peculiarity of its geological strata, lower chalk and upper gault to the east and various layers of lower greensand to the west of the town, the shelter afforded by hills and valleys with which the neighbourhood is so picturesquely embellished, the varied nature of the flora and above all its proximity to the coast of France, Folkestone offers a mine of wealth to the working entomologist; indeed there are few districts throughout the United Kingdom which have yielded such an imposing array of novel and rare species as has done this El Dorado of the British Lepidopterist. By way of illustration let me mention a few of the delicacies for which this locality is so justly famed.'

He mentions twelve moths, four of them macro-lepidoptera, that were discovered in this area before they were found anywhere else in this country, and twenty others that were then regarded as very rare or very local. He was able to produce a quite remarkable list of 325 species within a radius of six miles of the Town Hall, the usual criterion at a time when entomologists had to reach most of their collecting grounds on foot. This provides an area of less than fifty-seven square miles.

Ten years later, in his appendix to *Rambles of a Naturalist*, Ullyett produced a second list amounting to 533 species. This is a striking increase due, no doubt, to the work of many collectors, but the fact that it is a list of names only reduces its scientific value to not much more than nil. His excuse is that he feared over-collecting, a real danger at a time when the professional collector was rampant. Fifty-one years later the Society published an annotated list which I had drawn up after four years' residence in the town, during which time I had the good fortune to make the acquaintance of B. C. S. Warren, a world-wide authority on butterflies, and E. C. Joy from whom I received much help and advice and whose collection of British butterflies, now in the local museum, was regarded as the best one-man collection in the country.

Four years was not enough to make a thorough study of the area, especially as it had been increased to about one hundred and fifty-five square miles, on the principle that Romney Marsh as far as the Sussex border and Dungeness were now the proper province of the Folkestone Natural History Society, being by this time easily access-ible by car from Folkestone. So far this addition had brought only four names to our list which now totalled 561.

Romney Marsh and Dungeness were relatively little known at that time, but it was soon found that both contained much of interest to the entomologist. In 1934 Sir Beckwith Whitehouse and Mr Lee made such surprising captures at Dungeness that the place soon became famous, and nowadays there are few collectors who have not visited this and other parts of the Marsh.

The war years were, of course, barren years for our entomological section which had been very active since its foundation in 1937. In

1945 it resumed operations not only with members of long standing like Mr Warren, Dr Scott, Col Duffield, Mr Gilliat, Mr Pope, and Mr G. H. Youden, but also a succession of newer members including Mr Cue of Ashford, Mr Dudley Marsh of Herne Bay, Mr Bushby, formerly Keeper of the Insect House in the London Zoological Gardens, Mr Gummer of Deal, Mr Fawthrop and Mr L. W. Self, both of Folkestone. With their active help much was added to our knowledge of the lepidoptera of this Southern Triangle, and visiting entomologists were very ready to oblige us with information about their experiences in the area. By 1949 thirteen additions were made to our list in the Folkestone-Romney Marsh area alone.

The membership of the section has been sadly reduced, partly by death, partly by the departure of our keen young members to other spheres of activity, and partly by diminishing local interest in entomology. Yet in the period 1950–56 the names of twenty-eight species were added to our list. This was due to the use of a new invention, the mercury vapour lamp. The story goes that a Polish scientist, hiding in a wood to avoid the Germans and afraid to betray his position by using a bright light to attract the insects in which he was interested, tried the effect of using invisible ultra-violet rays, with the most gratifying results. After the war this successful experiment became known to our entomologists. At first they used the invisible rays, but as there were no Germans about and both the police and the general public regarded their activities as harmless, if eccentric, they soon came to use the bright lights of the mercury vapour lamp. Now in the summer Dungeness at night bears some resemblance to Piccadilly Circus.

Formerly entomologists collecting in the town made frequent use of the old-fashioned street lamps, especially the gas lamps, which attracted moths in large numbers and were easily accessible. This method ceased to be practicable when the present sophisticated street lamps were introduced, which, so far as my experience goes, have never yet attracted a moth and anyhow are quite out of reach.

In 1950 Professor A. G. Riddell set up one of the new mercury vapour lamps in his garden in Avereng Road and was kind enough to let me use it when he was at work in London. We both had high hopes, which were not disappointed. We had never expected to come across so many moths and in such variety. Soon afterwards Mr Fawthrop in Radnor Park Road followed suit and I did the same, so that at times there were three lamps at work each equipped with a

Robinson trap. The distance from the eastern to the western lamp was small, about three-fifths of a mile. Mr Robinson has estimated that the effective operation of these lamps extends to about fifty yards. I suppose this means an area of about an acre and a half in open ground but considerably less among houses. Thus between us we covered a very small part of the total area of the town, yet there were remarkable differences in what we found in our respective traps. It seems to be pretty certain that many moths, including not a few from a distance, fly at a high level and are attracted vertically as well as horizontally.

Among the species recently added the following are of particular interest:

THE TOADFLAX BROCADE *Calophasia lunula* Hufn

No more than five specimens of this moth had been captured between 1817 and 1951 when one was taken in Essex and another at Dungeness, where a second was taken in 1952. From that time the species has been found in considerable numbers, both in Essex and along the South Coast. In 1955 Miss Day, the Society's Honorary Secretary, found about a dozen caterpillars on linaria in her garden and in 1962 Nigel Reay Jones took a moth at Sandgate. This moth occurs in central Europe and in Asia from Armenia to Amurland.

THE VARIED CORONET *Hadena compta* Schiff

Very few specimens of this moth were known in this country until W. Purdey took one at Lydden Spout in 1877. In the following year one was taken in South Devon and apparently no other until G. H. Youden caught eleven in his garden in Dover in 1948. Many occurred there in 1949 and two caterpillars were found on the Folkestone Downs. Both moths and caterpillars have since been found fairly regularly in Folkestone. This insect occurs in central and southern Europe, and as far east as Japan. Since its discovery in Dover, it has spread quite rapidly over south and east England. This species is illustrated on the final plate of this book, together with the marbled coronet, a common moth in Southern England, which is very similar in appearance.

THE GIANT EAR *Gortyna hucherardi* Mab

The first specimen of this moth to be taken in England was found on a street lamp in Hailsham by David Saunders, formerly of Hythe, sometime before 1953, in which year one was found on Romney Marsh by W. F. Tweedie and one at Dungeness by H. Robinson. Later it was found to occur in considerable numbers in certain parts of the Marsh. This is a most remarkable moth, for it is so large that it could not easily escape notice, and yet wherever it came from it would take years at least to become so widespread. Moreover, according to Seitz, it is known from no other place in the world but Royan in Western France. Its caterpillar feeds on the roots of Marsh Mallow.

THE SUSSEX EMERALD *Thalera fimbrialis* Scop
The first specimen of the Sussex emerald alias notched emerald, a pretty light bright green moth, was taken at Beachy Head in 1902, a second at Swanage in 1936, a third at Bournemouth in 1940, and a fourth at Bradwell in Essex. During the night of 28th July 1950 G. H. Youden and I took one female and five males flying at Dungeness. During the following few nights, we were joined by two other members of the section, and between us we had found sixteen of these moths. It looks as if the species, having tried to settle in different parts of Southern England, has at last found a place that suits it. It occurs on heaths in central Europe and central Asia. In Denmark it is said to prefer the sea coast to inland heaths. Its presence at Dungeness has made that locality more popular than ever.

THE WHITE-BANDED CARPET *Euphyia luctuata* Schiff
Another newcomer is the white-banded carpet moth, of which one was taken in North Kent in 1924 and another in Essex. No more were seen until 1950 when a second was taken in Kent and two on the coast of Sussex. In the following year, one was found in a moth-trap in Folkestone on the morning of 2nd August, and three others were taken in Kent between 1st August and 1st September, all I imagine within easy reach of Ashford, where it became common. Apparently the numbers have increased considerably both in Kent and in Sussex. That is certainly true of Reinden Wood, where nineteen were noted in 1953 and others since then. In 1954, R. W. Fawthrop took two in his garden. This history of this moth seems to be parallel to that of the preceding, though their habitats differ and so does their distribution, for this one occurs in central and northern Europe including arctic Norway, Esthonia and Northern Finland, and is

found also in Central Asia, Labrador, and Western Canada. The caterpillar feeds on willowherb and bedstraw.

THE YARROW PUG *Eupithecia millefoliata* Rossl
The first British specimen was taken in 1933 by Dr de Worms in a wood not far from Ashford, and a second by one of our leading entomologists, Mr Austin Richardson at Sandwich on 15th July 1939. The pugs are small moths, many of which are not at all easy to identify, and the true identity of these two specimens was not known until 1948 when three specimens were bred by Mr Wakely from caterpillars found on yarrow near Ramsgate. In 1950 a small caterpillar was found at the nearest part of the Hythe rifle range, and towards the end of September, forty-five larger ones were found between that point and the Redoubt. A few days later two were found on the Folkestone Golf Course. In the following year, twenty-four caterpillars were found in the latter place, and three moths were taken in Folkestone at night. In this same year, Mr Haggett obtained twelve caterpillars along the road to Dover, twelve in Cherry Garden Avenue, and one near Dymchurch. I believe that caterpillars and moths were taken at Dungeness, but perhaps the best locality of all was a piece of waste ground near the golf course where a year or two later about fifty caterpillars were found on a rich growth of yarrow. Not long afterwards, the place was burnt out as a result of a favourite amusement of the local children, when there is a dry spell in the autumn. Since those days, in recent years, the moth has spread along the coast as far as Hampshire, and inland as far as Canterbury and Essex. Abroad, the moth inhabits central and southern Europe, Asia Minor and Transcaucasia.

THREE JUNIPER MOTHS
In the last fourteen years three moths turned up which are well known in Scotland, but not previously recorded in this area. The first is the juniper pug, *Eupithecia sobrinata* Hubn, which formerly occurred at Dover, not in recent years, but still maintains a rather precarious existence in Mrs Scott's garden at Westwell. The second is the Edinburgh pug, *Eupithecia intricata* Zett, common enough in Scotland, but in England existing in the form of a sub-species much larger and formerly regarded as a rare and different species. In Surrey, I failed to find the caterpillar on juniper, but found one on *Cupressus macrocarpa*, and about twenty on thuya. This new species

appeared also in Mr P. Cue's garden at Ashford in 1956. The last of the three is the juniper carpet, *Thera juniperata* Linn, of which one came to light in Folkestone in 1965, and two in the following year. This moth is so much larger than the Scottish specimens that at first sight it might be mistaken for a different species. It is not suggested that any of these have come here from abroad. They are probably immigrants from another part of Kent or a neighbouring county, and it may be assumed that they have taken to various forms of cypress in the absence of juniper and gained in size as a result.

FOLKESTONE SPECIALITIES

The first of what may be termed Folkestone's specialities is the fiery clearwing, *Aegeria chrysidiformis* Esp, which Knaggs calls 'this glorious clearwing' and which was once not very appropriately known as the ruby clearwing. What was probably the first genuine English specimen was taken in the Warren in 1856 by a Mr Brewer, a collector of beetles, who put it in his tobacco tin. There have been records of three other specimens since then: one at Eastbourne in 1874, a second in the Forest of Dean in 1902, while in a recently published book there is a reference to its occurrence in Herne Bay. Knaggs, in his 1870 list, says 'not scarce at present'. This species belongs to a strange and perhaps rather primitive group of moths, which have wings largely denuded of scales, whence their English name. They all seem to mimic or resemble other insects such as wasps, hornets, ichneumon flies, etc. This is their form of self protection. The caterpillars are internal feeders, living inside or under the bark of tree trunks, or in stems of bushes or in roots. The fiery clearwing, though small, is one of the prettiest of them, having on its forewings except for the central area, bright vermillion scales. It is not easy to find, but it was persisting in fair numbers in 1946 and is probably still to be found in the Warren, though under existing conditions I would not bank on its continued survival.

In the late 1920s and the early 1930s, Folkestone was well known to every collector of butterflies and visited regularly by most of them. The attraction was the little adonis blue, *Lysandra bellargus* Rott, which to my mind is one of the most beautiful butterflies in the world, comparable, except for its size, with the famous morpho butterflies of Brazil, which are, I suppose, about twenty times as big. Ullyett in his *Rambles* describes how, in the light of the afternoon sun, he stood on the Downs beyond the waterworks and saw the whole

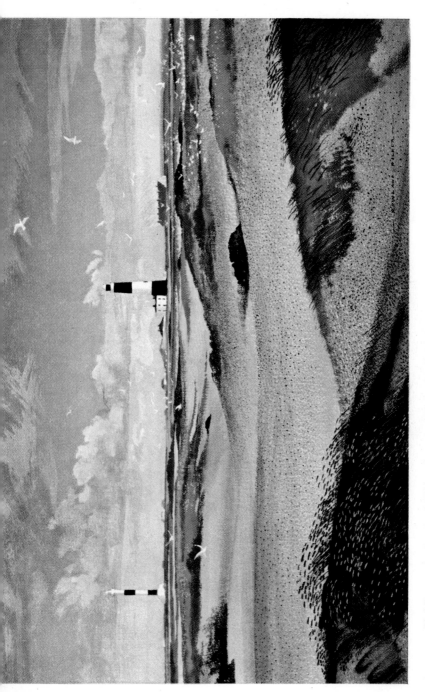

Dungeness Bird Reserve by Rowland Hilder. *Courtesy of Shell-Mex & BP Ltd.*

Top: Ringing in progress at Dungeness.
Bottom: Guillemots. *Courtesy of CEGB.*

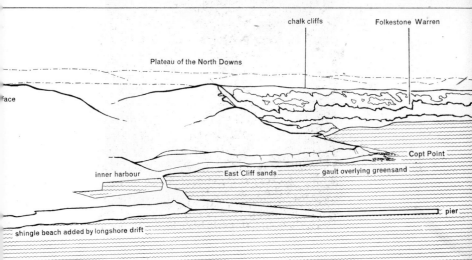

chalk cliffs   Folkestone Warren

Plateau of the North Downs

face

Copt Point

inner harbour   East Cliff sands   gault overlying greensand

pier

shingle beach added by longshore drift

Approach to the Downs.

Top to bottom: British *Hadena compta*, wing span 1⅛ ins; *Hadena conspersa*; and Chalk Hill Blue.

slope below him covered with innumerable adonis blues, with their wings outspread, resting on the grass in the western sunlight. Such things did not happen every year, for the species sometimes nearly died out, and then increased steadily in number. It did so from 1928 to its peak year of 1933, when one morning I counted fourteen entomologists at work. Mr L. W. Newman, the famous professional, used to stay in Folkestone every year and spend many hours a day examining these butterflies. One day in 1933 he told me that he caught and looked at over two thousand specimens. He was of course looking for varieties or specimens that were out of the ordinary in some way or other. I used to estimate that one butterfly in two hundred was perhaps good enough to keep, and one in one thousand would be a rarity. Mr Newman told me that on average, he earned enough to pay for his lodgings while here. Unfortunately, the numbers began to decline in subsequent years, and fewer entomologists thought it worth while to pay a visit. At the beginning of the Second World War a deep trench was dug by the Army along the Downs to serve as a trap for a possible attack by German tanks. Unfortunately for our butterfly, its principal breeding ground was dug up, and much of the hippocrepis on which the caterpillars feed was destroyed.

A second butterfly which has attracted entomologists to Folkestone is the chalk hill blue, *Lysandra coridon* Poda. This is a larger and more powerful insect than the adonis blue. Consequently, it is more widespread, though always on chalk or limestone. On our Downs, both butterflies occur in the Warren and on either side of the Dover Road. In fact, the older collectors looked for them on this part of the Downs. Probably in the 1920s, it was found that the Middle Hill, sheltered from the wind and open to the sun, was a far better place for the adonis blue and collectors moved there and paid little attention to the East Downs. In 1932, Newman, by pure chance visited a steep and windswept part of these Downs, and found one or two melanic specimens. These are sometimes called the Folkestone black, of a very unusual if not unique form, since they are melanic below as well as above. He told Mr Joy about these, who soon found two of these rarities, and very kindly invited another friend and me to join him in the good work. Neither of us could find a melanic one, but I did find a grey one which, as it happened, proved to be even rarer than the others. Many visitors came to look for these rarities, but few succeeded. After all, the chance of finding one was not great, for so far as I know, no more than twenty-four were taken in the twenty-four years that ended with the disappearance of this form and most of the species in that particular area in 1956. It is probable that one cause was once again the destruction by fire of a considerable area of vegetation in August 1955, in the very centre of the locality, where practically all the melanic specimens had been found. Both these blues vary considerably, and the chalk hill blue is by a long way the most variable of our butterflies. A large and expensive book has been published on its many divergent forms. The two butterflies are much alike in the shape of the egg, and the caterpillars of both feed on hippocrepis, and are associated with ants. In most books on entomology the two species are placed next to each other, though they differ in so far as the adonis blue is the more southern of the two, occurring in North Africa, as well as Southern Europe, and has two broods in the year as against the one of the chalk hill blue.

A. G. Side FLS

6

MOSSES and LIVERWORTS
in the District

Full many a flower is born to blush unseen,
And waste its sweetness on the desert air.

Gray was, of course, speaking of flowers in unexplored countries
when he wrote these lines. Had he been a bryologist he would have
realized that in this country, within the range of crowds of people,
there are treasures of sweetness which very few bother to look at.
On the ploughland of the downs above Folkestone, for example,
when fields are fallow in winter anyone could see *Phascum cuspidatum,*
Pottia truncata, Dicranella varia or *Barbula unguiculata,* common plants
to be found on any chalky arable land. Each of these plants when
looked at with adequate magnification is seen to be most beautiful,
yet even people who are keen naturalists and specialize in botany
have perhaps never looked at any of them. In the latest published
list of members of the British Bryological Society, among the four
hundred and twenty-six named, less than twenty live in Kent. To
one who has been fascinated by the delicacy of mosses and liverworts for some years there is something sad in the thought that so
much is being missed by so many.

Much of the beauty of bryophytes can be seen with the aid of
nothing more expensive than a hand lens, though it is true that a
dissecting microscope, with objectives capable of giving magnifica-
tions up to 180, is necessary for the really serious study of bryology,
together with a few books to help in identification. Less than twenty

years ago these books were not available, but during the last two decades Dixon's *Handbook of British Mosses* and MacVicar's *Handbook of British Hepatics* have been reprinted, while E. V. Watson has published a new book *British Mosses & Liverworts* to help in identification. This last not only explains to beginners what bryophytes are and how to identify them, but also has a separate key which can be used in the field, as well as hints on collecting and preserving the plants. A dissecting microscope and the necessary books could be bought for less than many people pay for a television set, or for what many smokers spend in a year on reputed coffin nails. A microscope does not depreciate in value over the years. Students who are willing to go to the length of saving for such a microscope and books need no more encouragement for they will find their reward in their studies.

It is impossible to describe the beauty and fascination of bryophytes to anyone who has not looked at them with a hand lens which magnifies at least ten times. They are spore-bearing plants and so have two alternating generations. Unlike the ferns the two generations are not entirely independent. The second generation is always found growing on the first. The first generation which bears the male and female inflorescences is always green and leafy in the mosses. It is often leafy in the liverworts, though there are many species in which the plant is not differentiated into stem and leaf, and there is at least one British liverwort, to be mentioned later, which has no green chlorophyll. The second generation consists of a spore-bearing capsule borne on a stalk. In the liverworts this stalk lengthens suddenly taking the ripe capsule aloft when it is ready to burst. In the mosses the stalk grows slowly and the capsule is not formed nor the spores ripened until the stalk has lengthened. In some species of moss, however, the stalk is so short as to appear non-existent, and then the ripe capsule has to be looked for among the green leaves of the first generation.

The capsules of mosses are varied and beautiful. Usually there is a cap which, when the spores are ripe, falls off revealing the peristome teeth beneath. It is a most fascinating sight to see these teeth, which control the release of spores from the capsule, opening and closing when atmospheric conditions are right, so that the spores are discharged. Again, looked at with the proper magnification, it is difficult to imagine anything more beautiful in construction than the peristomes of mosses. For some idea of the variety of capsules and of the forms of peristome teeth a little King Penguin *A Book of Mosses* by P. Richards is recommended. It is illustrated with pictures taken from the plates published in Germany in 1787–97 by Johannes Hedwig, one of the most famous of the early bryologists. The short text of this book is a scholarly introduction to the study of mosses.

The south-eastern corner of Britain is not the best part in which to see bryophytes. They are plants which flourish in the moister, cleaner air of the north and west of the British Isles and are among the first to feel the effects of air pollution caused by human habitation and industrial fumes. The clearing of ground for building destroys their habitat and altogether they have a pretty lean time in well-farmed Kent. In the countryside of the Folkestone area, as in the rest of the Weald, there are many different soils producing habitats where bryophytes can flourish. It is not the intention of this article to give a list of the mosses to be found in the area. This has already been done by E. C. Green, 'Mosses of the Folkestone District', *South East Naturalist & Antiquary*, Vol. LV. Readers of his paper will find that, as with the vascular plants, some names have changed since he wrote it. To ease this situation Richards and Wallace have drawn up a list of mosses giving the new names together with the old synonyms, 'An Annotated List of British Mosses' in *Transactions of the British Bryological Society*, *1*.4.(i). It is my hope to point to work which is still to be done. That most indefatigable field worker Dr Francis Rose is engaged at present in listing the bryophytes to be found in every ten-kilometre square in Kent, a most exciting study. Three of the most interesting mosses in Kent, *Leptodon smithii*, *Antitrichia curtipendula* and *Scorpiurium circinatum* are at present known in Kent only in two or three squares, all of which fall within the Folkestone area. Several other interesting ones are found more abundantly in this area than anywhere else in the county.

Lest one should be tempted to think that every moss and liverwort in Kent has been found and mapped long ago I would quote the case of a foreign botanist who landed at Dover in August 1957. Having a little time to spare between the time he left the boat and the time he entered his train, he inspected the chalk blocks at the foot of Dover cliffs. He found there a liverwort known previously only from Dorset, East and West Sussex, and West Gloucester. The faces of English, and especially Kentish, botanists turned a little red.

In 1957 Mr E. C. Wallace reported that he had been finding on chalk rubble a small mediterranean species of moss, *Tortella inflexa*, never before seen in Britain. This plant appears to be spreading.

Since the beginning of 1961 I have been looking for it, successfully in Kent. In April 1962 I found it west of Dover on a sheltered hillside and in April 1964 on a chalk stone in Folkestone Warren. These are sure signs that there is still much to look for and that no one can be sure of what will turn up.

In Britain species are still being found which are new to science. As recently as 1965 *Fissidens celticus* was described by Mrs Jean Paton as a new species. This plant has already, in 1966, been hunted down in the Benenden and Cranbrook areas of Kent. It likes steep, shaded banks above streams on loamy, non-basic soils. Who, now, can find such a habitat in the Folkestone area and this plant growing in it? The saprophytic liverwort, *Cryptothallus mirabilis*, which has no green chlorophyll, was found in Britain for the first time in 1948, but it is now known to be widespread. It was found in Kent for the first time in 1966, in the Biddenden and Cranbrook areas. It grows on raw humus in wet places, often under *Sphagnum*. There must be places where it could be found in the Folkestone area. Such challenges are to be met by those who undertake the rewarding task of studying bryophytes. For what it is worth I counted the number of contributors of New County Records in the latest *Transactions of the British Bryological Society*. Fifty-nine were men and seventeen were women. I wonder if any conclusions can be drawn from these figures?

H. M. Rowland

7

BIRD WATCHING
around Folkestone

A bird-minded visitor to the Folkestone area stands a good chance of seeing many interesting birds, if only for two reasons. Firstly because the area contains four main types of country which are completely different: the chalk Downs which terminate in the sea cliffs near Dover; the Warren; the Marsh; and the Lowlands, each with its characteristic birds. Secondly, this area lies at the junction of several great aerial highways and so migration may be watched not only in spring and autumn but in ten months out of every twelve.

This part of Kent is very favourably situated for the autumn passage, because birds leaving the north and north-eastern parts of Europe travel south and south-west following the continental coast-lines and crossing into the comparatively mild parts of Europe bordering the Atlantic. Many cross over into Kent when they reach the Channel. We therefore not only receive birds which winter with us, but we lie in the direct path of these passage migrants. Certain weather conditions such as low thick cloud, rain, or a sudden change of wind direction, especially to the east, may bring the flights of migrating birds down. When this happens, the bushes along the coast may become alive with warblers, spotted and pied flycatchers, wheatears, goldcrests, redstarts, whinchats and others. Then it may be possible to see the continental races of the jay, chaffinch, robin, song thrush, hedgesparrow, long-tailed tit and many more. At such times the occasional rarity may be seen, such as the bluethroat or great grey shrike, both of which have actually been seen in Folkestone.

The hoopoe nested in Hythe in 1948 and 1949. The grey wagtail has nested in Hythe for many years and rarities like the black-winged stilt, black-bellied dipper, rose-coloured starling, crane, avocet and black-necked grebe turn up there when least expected, just to keep local ornithologists alert.

At the end of the Second World War, black redstarts commonly nested in the bombed buildings in the Dover area. As the ruins were rebuilt the black redstart became rarer as a nesting species, but is still regularly seen on migration.

The golden oriole visits the South of England annually in small numbers, and as its visits are most frequent in this county, there may be a chance that it will one day become a regular nesting species in the cherry orchards of Kent.

These are some of the highlights which may or may not be seen. Now consider the resident and regular bird visitors to the area.

THE DOWNS

Larks and meadow pipits are the common birds of the chalk plateau of the Downs. Yellow hammers and linnets nest in any of the low gorse bushes. Where the ridge of the Downs comes to the sea it forms cliffs, and here some cliff-nesting birds are found. Herring gulls nest on the ledges and where no cliff ledges are available they nest on the roofs and chimney stacks of buildings. Fulmars nest in holes in the cliffs beyond St Margaret's Bay. Until the use of lethal sprays reduced their numbers peregrines and kestrels also nested on the ledges of the chalk cliffs. Now peregrines are extremely rare and kestrels are commonly seen only during the autumn and winter when their numbers are increased by birds from the Continent. At these times kestrels are often to be seen hovering over the Downs.

In spring and early summer it is not very unusual to hear a three-note call sounding like 'quic-quic-ic' or 'wet-mi-lips' coming from some downland field. This is the call of the quail and being very elusive it is more likely to be heard than seen.

THE WARREN

The Warren is sheltered and has many thick bushes. Because of this it has a rich variety of small birds such as thrushes, bullfinches, green-finches, linnets, wrens, blackbirds, hedgesparrows and tits. In spring, willow warblers, chiff-chaffs, blackcaps, common and lesser white-throats, cuckoos and turtle doves swell their numbers.

The bird population here is rather similar to that of the bushy sloping face of the Leas at Folkestone. There are no really unusual species, but as elsewhere in the area there is a good chance of a rarity turning up, given the right weather conditions and season of the year. Large numbers of gulls, including some of the lesser known kinds, skuas, terns, divers, ducks, grebes and auks (especially guillemots), pass along the English Channel during migration periods and some spend the winter in its waters. These can all be seen at various times from any part of the coast from the Warren right round the bay towards Dungeness Point. However, it is at the Point itself where they can be watched most easily and in the greatest numbers, because here they tend to come closer inshore. It is possible to watch at least six different kinds of terns from the Point: sandwich, common, arctic, roseate, little and black; and if it is your lucky day you may have the excitement of seeing a robber skua fly in and chase the terns.

THE MARSH

The Marsh may be considered under four headings: the fertile fields, the foreshore, gravel areas, fresh-water pools.

FERTILE FIELDS In winter the fields of Romney Marsh are usually covered with lapwings, golden plovers and the winter-visiting thrushes: fieldfares, redwings, missel thrushes, song thrushes and blackbirds. In irruption years waxwings often reach Kent and then the heavily berried hawthorn hedges of the marsh roads attracts these lovely birds. Hard weather brings geese but they are not regular winter visitors to this part of Kent. Yellow wagtails arrive in April and spend the summer on the fields and damper areas of the marsh.

FORESHORE The foreshore from Dymchurch to Dungeness is a good place for waders. Flocks of curlews, oyster catchers, grey plovers, ringed plovers, knots, turnstones, redshank, bar-tailed godwits, dunlin and sanderling are generally to be seen there. Other waders prefer shallow, marshy pools rather than the actual seashore, such as the Wicks near Camber. Regular watching there should enable one to see the magnificent black-tailed godwit, whimbrel, ruff, snipe, woodsandpiper, little stint, curlew sandpiper, greenshank and dusky redshank. Ducks of all kinds also visit these pools and one may be lucky enough to see the beautiful little garganey which, unlike all our other ducks, only spends the spring and summer in this country.

The south coast of Kent between Folkestone and Pett Level is on the edge of the range of the kentish plover which is a small wader common in suitable localities round the coasts of Europe. Disturbance due to development along our stretch of coast has destroyed its nesting places and it is only seen now as a rare passage migrant.

GRAVEL AREAS Where undisturbed the gravel areas provide nesting sites for little and common terns, ringed plovers, oyster catchers, lapwings, common, herring and black-headed gulls. Unless in a protected area these larger nests are too easily seen and often get destroyed. It is interesting to note the three very different nesting sites chosen by the herring gull in the Folkestone area: ledges of cliffs, chimney stacks of buildings and on the shingle.

Wheatears make their nests down disused rabbit holes or under old tins, etc. Shelduck also nest down the rabbit holes and are common in suitable places all over Romney Marsh. The shingle areas have usually been the home of a few pairs of stone curlews but in recent years this bird has become scarcer.

The large area of shingle south of Lydd is often very interesting in winter. It is possible to see such rarities as the rough-legged buzzard, hen harrier or merlin wintering there, while short-eared owls and kestrels are generally common. These birds of prey usually feed on small rodents and birds, which are both plentiful in this area. Large flocks of greenfinches, linnets and sometimes twites spend the winter here.

Snow buntings are attracted by the seeds of the sea beet growing along the coast from the Wicks to the dunes at Camber.

FRESH-WATER POOLS Where gravel quarrying has been in operation, deep fresh water pools are formed. Although artificial, they are often stocked with fish by anglers and prove very attractive to birds. Many species of duck visit these pools in winter, including wigeon, teal, mallard, shovelers, pintail, smew, tufted duck, pochard, common scoters and the rarer velvet scoter. Storm-driven sea-birds such as long-tailed duck, various divers and grebes occasionally arrive. Mute swans, great crested grebes, dabchick and coot nest in the shallower parts and the gravel islands provide safer nesting sites for the terns than the open shingle.

In winter herds of mute swans collect together and look most spectacular flying over the Marsh. Bewick and whooper swans are occasional visitors.

Dividing Romney Marsh from the minor escarpment which marks

the ancient coastline, runs the Royal Military Canal. Herons fish along the edge and water rails skulk through the marshy ground near by. Until the cold winter of 1963–4 kingfishers were very common, but the cold nearly wiped them out. Redshank feed along the canal's muddy edges and common and green sandpipers are often seen on migration. In winter grey wagtails frequent the canal but they leave in spring to nest by hillside streams. The alders growing along the banks attract wintering flocks of lesser redpolls and siskins which like to feed on the cones. A walk from the Hythe Miniature Railway along the canal to Botolph's Bridge may be quite rewarding in the variety of birds it produces.

Owls are well represented on the Marsh. In autumn the numbers of short-eared owls in this country are augmented by birds from the continent and many of these may be seen hunting over the fields or shingle in winter. Sometimes, when the vole supply is good, they are extremely common. Little owls too are seen in good numbers all over the area.

Only a few years ago barn owls were a familiar sight hunting along the marshland dykes, but now they are rare birds due to the farmer's use of toxic chemicals. There are, however, encouraging signs that there may be a slight increase in their numbers since the use of chemicals has been restricted.

Sedge and reed warblers frequent some of the clumps of reeds which grow along the edges of the dykes and pools. Reed buntings, too, are common and the corn bunting may be found in rough fields nearer the coast.

THE LOWLANDS

Lying between the chalk escarpment of the Downs and the Marsh is a countryside of woods, fields and villages. From the woods in spring comes a chorus of willow warblers, chiffchaffs, blackcaps, garden warblers and nightingales, though the latter are much less common than they were. Treecreepers, wrens and hedgesparrows are all plentiful but nuthatches are rather scarce. Three kinds of woodpecker (green, greater and lesser spotted) were common until the severe winter of 1963–4 when their numbers were seriously reduced. They are slowly increasing now.

Great, blue and coal tits are common and family parties of long-tailed tits join them as they travel through the trees.

Round the farmlands greenfinches, house- and tree-sparrows are abundant with a fair number of chaffinches. Wherever there are teasels or thistles charms of goldfinches are to be found. In winter bramblings from the far north may often be found searching for beech mast or feeding on any rough stubble, probably in company with chaffinches.

The hooting of the tawny owl is often heard where there are enough trees to provide suitable nesting holes.

The crow family is well represented. Rooks, carrion crows, jackdaws, magpies and jays are to be seen everywhere although the carrion crow is commoner on the shingle areas near the sea. Hundreds of greater and lesser black-backed, herring, common and black-headed gulls feed and rest on the fields. In winter, the common gull is the most numerous on these Lowland fields.

A bird-watcher to the Folkestone area would almost certainly hope to see the wryneck, because Kent is the last stronghold of this fascinating bird, but unfortunately this area is rapidly losing its nesting wrynecks. A few males can still be heard calling during April, but, as is always the case when a species is withdrawing from a territory, the hen birds leave first and the males visit the area and linger for a while but soon leave also. Ten years ago wrynecks were nesting in suitable holes in fruit trees or nesting boxes all over the district.

With its wonderful position right in the path of the hordes of migrating birds and its great diversity of types of country, the Folkestone area could hardly fail to provide good bird-watching.

A. E. Clough

8

BADGERS
near Denton

For some years I have been watching badgers near Denton. In a square mile or so, which I have tried to keep under observation, there are some six setts comprising about twenty-three holes. This number varies from year to year. In the same area of woodland, parkland, and arable land, are numerous other holes, some occupied regularly by foxes and others occupied intermittently by badgers.

When taking a walk across this area through the dense coppice, across the pastures, beside the ponds and along the overhanging shaws one can see much evidence of the badgers' nocturnal activities. Near the setts and sometimes at a distance from them the well-defined runs made during the nightly foraging excursions may be found, and at intervals along these runs are the familiar scrapes where the badgers have dug out roots or small animals for food. Outside the sett itself there is usually a platform of excavated earth, stones, and chalk, and on this is often found bedding such as leaves and grass, which has been dropped when being brought into the sett, or taken out when the sett has become soiled. There is no smell, apart from a slight earthy odour, and no litter of decaying bones and flesh such as is frequently found outside a fox's hole. A favourite scratching tree or log is often seen near the sett and beside the ponds there are well-worn tracks where the badgers come to drink.

Much can be found out about the badgers even before one spends a few hours sitting outside the sett at dusk. When following the runs through fences, tufts of hair are often left by the badgers in the

barbed wire and on brambles. In his monograph *The Badger* (Colli
1948) Neal mentions the colouring of the hair which, he asser
differs with the age of the animal, though this is not an infallib
test. It was thought that the more white on the hair, the older tl
badger. Although badgers are usually black and white the Folkesto1
Museum has two specimens, caught locally, one of which is ;
albino with the hair a yellowish-white as in a ferret, and the oth
an erythristic form in which the black is replaced by a sandy r
colour. A yellowish form is also known to occur.

At a short distance from each sett are the dung pits. By carryi1
out a number of tests, including dung analysis, Neal showed th
badgers do little harm on farms. I made a number of these analy:
and found the following had been eaten: worms, beetles, chrysalis
wasps, bumble bees, young rabbits, oats, leaves, flowers, barl
various roots, grass, various seeds, and some small stones. The lat
were probably eaten when the animal was digging up roots. One
the analyses was composed almost entirely of a saucerful of unri
barley husks, while another was composed almost completely of t
remains of wasps.

Numbers of badgers have been shot in the area, some skins bei
sent away, the hair to be used for shaving brushes. Some have be
gin-trapped by gamekeepers; one was tossed and killed by a c
just after the cow had calved; one was found dead under a stra
stack; and one found its way into a hen hut, could not get o
snapped at and killed a number of pullets, and was shot by
farmer's wife. Apart from this there was interference by sh
farmers trying to dig out the setts under the impression that
badgers killed the young lambs when all the evidence showed tl
foxes were the cause of the trouble. A newly-born lamb was fou
half eaten on one of the farms in the area. Suspicion for this res
on the badgers but, as the enlightened farmer on whose land
occurred pointed out, there is nothing to show that the lamb was
already dead when it was eaten, as so many other lambs die e;
year in the cold winter winds. However, the local Pest Officer visi
this farm and, among the pests he enumerated, badgers were n
the top of the list. And so the persecution goes on. On reconstruct
the skeleton of a badger, two years after it had been run ove
found a .22 bullet hole through the skull. What agony this ani
must have suffered before being mercifully killed! After the Can
bury to Dover railway line was electrified there were few badger

the area for a year or two. The local Pest Officer was blamed for
their disappearances. He found from railway linesmen that seventy
or eighty badgers had been killed between Canterbury and Dover
after the first year of electrification.

In the early days of watching I read that badgers were very fond
of honey, treacle and aniseed. Hoping to attract the badgers to a
spot where a trip wire would operate the camera and flashbulbs, a
friend and I tried putting down empty jam and honey tins, but with
no result, except that next morning a farmworker from some
distance away said to me, 'There was a funny smell of aniseed balls
here last night when I came home!'

I find the best conditions for watching are bright moonlight and
little or no wind. The watcher need not sit behind cover, but he
must remain perfectly still down-wind from the sett, preferably
getting in position before sunset. The time of emergence seems to
vary with the position of the sett—whether near to or remote from
habitation, whether the badgers are persecuted or not, or whether it
is a still or windy night. There are three conditions for emergence:
confidence, weather, and time of year, though hunger must play
some part in this. Just at sunset, when the robin and blackbird have
sung their vespers and the initial screeches of owls have died away,
there is a period of quiet when the badger tests the air before
emerging. On a still evening this testing takes place outside the hole.
On a windy night it presumably takes place just inside the hole. The
time of year also has a great effect on emergence. Badgers evidently
do not like getting wet, and prefer to stay in longer in rough weather.

The best months of the year to watch badgers, are April, May,
and June, when the cubs are young and play on the platform outside
the sett. One of the adults emerges first and tests the air. This is
followed by a period of scratching as, according to Neal, the badger
is said to be one of the only animals which shares with man the
privilege of harbouring the common flea *Pulex irritans*, but he is also
a very clean animal and, according to Mr R. Sankey BSc, the
scratching is due to a dry scurfy skin. By this time the other adult and
the young are out on the platform, and in a few minutes the cubs are
in full play, butting each other, rushing round and round, playing
leap-frog and scratching the bark off their favourite log or tree.

Badgers do not seem to make much noise. I have heard occasional
grunts by the adults and higher pitched squeaks by the young on one
or two occasions when they have been playing. When the sow was

near, she made a peculiar noise which I would describe as a low grumbling chuckle. Other observers have described it as a purring noise. This seemed to be for a number of purposes as the tempo and timbre were altered. When one youngster butted the sow while she was scratching, she turned on it with this grumbling noise uttered loudly. When the youngsters were playing contentedly, the noise was much lower, and when they strayed away the sow went after them making this noise. At the sett entrance, she would look them over soon after emergence and emit this grumbling, purring noise again. Other observers record badgers shrieking.

On one occasion, after two youngsters had been playing for some time, the sow appeared to want them to go back into the hole, presumably while she went off foraging. She held one of the youngsters by the ear and pulled it down the hole, and went back for the other. While dragging the second in, against its will, the first shot out of the hole and began playing again. This continued until eventually she managed to get her unruly youngsters underground.

On other occasions, a badger has emerged and gone straight into the undergrowth, returning a few minutes later dragging a heap of leaves under its fore-paws backwards down the hole. It has repeated this and also torn off large pieces of dog's mercury. Presumably it did not matter whether the bedding was dry or green. On one occasion it was bright moonlight, and although only six or eight yards away, I watched the badger's every movement through binoculars. Some observers have experienced excellent watching by shining torches on the badgers. The first occasion on which my wife and I took our children they fell asleep and their snoring kept the badgers in. On the next occasion the badgers emerged in daylight and the children were very excited, but kept still nevertheless.

Badgers make excellent pets if they can be obtained very young, as Mr Sankey has shown us from his excellent film. If obtained too late it is impossible to train them. A Denton farmer caught one and it was kept for two or three weeks in a large shed, but as it was so restless and untameable it was released. A few nights later it returned to the farm, was seen by another farmworker, and promptly shot.

Photography is not conducive to successful badger watching. It is necessary, of course, to use flashlight and this frightens the badgers for a time although it is surprising, if the photographer makes very little noise, how soon the badgers reappear after the flash.

Once, when taking a photograph of two young badgers playing,

Three moths commonly seen in the area: *left*, the White Spot, almost unique to Dungeness; *centre*, the Hawk Moth; *right*, the immigrant Silver Y. *Courtesy of CEGB.*

Late Spider Orchid.

Lizard Orchid.

one of them ran back into the sett after the flash, while the other sneezed several times and returned to the sett only after I shone my torch. Within minutes they were out again playing. This gave time to re-set the camera and prepare for another photograph. It is, of course, more interesting, although there is less to show for it, to sit and watch badgers without taking photographs.

An hour's quiet watching is a worth-while experience. There is always something to see to interest the naturalist. We live at such a tempo that an hour of solitude in the country is both aesthetically and spiritually satisfying.

9

FISH
off the Coast

The history of the fishing industry in the area comprising Dungeness Point to Shakespeare Cliff would make very interesting reading. An extract from the accounts of George Miller dated May 1659, reads as follows: 'To repairing 10 Herring nets — 1/–d.' In today's world this would cost approximately £10. The main species of fish now caught are plaice, skate, dogfish, turbot, cod and dover soles, with herrings, sprats and mackerel in the migration season. Of the shellfish lobsters, common edible crab and whelks are the most plentiful.

The fishing grounds in the area are good, the most common being Dungeness Bay, Hythe Bay, East Wear Bay, Varne Banks and La Cobalt — The Ridge. The fish are caught by several methods, namely bottom trawling for soles, plaice, cod, skate, turbot; line fishing on the Ridge Banks for turbot, cod, skate and gurnard; drift net for herring, sprats and mackerel; and pots for lobsters and edible crab.

Trawling is carried on by a few boats all the year round, using a funnel-like pocket net towed slowly behind the craft so that the fish pass into the mouth of the net and down into the cod end.

Long line fishing is practised during autumn, winter and early spring. The lines are approximately one hundred fathoms long containing one hundred hooks, spaced at one-fathom intervals. These are baited into baths at shore with either sprat, herring, whelk or squid, then shot over the stern of the craft to lie on the bottom. Each boat has upwards of forty-eight lines, totalling four or five miles in length. It is the commonest method used by the fishing boats in this area. The biggest enemy to line fishing is the trawler which fouls the lines, also gale force winds which tangle them up. Otherwise this is a profitable method of fishing and has been carried on for a hundred years or more.

Lobsters, crabs and whelks are caught in pots especially designed for the purpose with floats and dahn strings. The smaller type of open motor fishing craft is mainly used.

At the present time the numbers of boats employed at the different ports along the coast are approximately as follows:

	full-time		*part-time*	
	boats	*men*	*boats*	*men*
Folkestone	16	36	6	12
Hythe	5	8	5	10
Dungeness	22	28	3	6

So far the erection of the Nuclear Power Station at Dungeness Point has had little effect on fishing. It was objected that intake water damaged some of the fishing but steps have been taken to remedy this.

Foreign trawlers from France, Belgium and Germany operate in the area sometimes; also during migration the herring fleet operates in large numbers and makes Dover its headquarters.

The twelve-mile international limit is in operation and only British vessels of under twenty tons can fish within the three-mile limit.

Fish which are rare in these waters but sometimes caught include sturgeon, shad, haddock, lamp sucker, angler, monkfish and garfish. In 1965 a twenty-pound sturgeon was caught and under Act of Parliament was offered to the Queen.

It is possible to arrange a day out in a fishing boat, a trawler trip taking twelve to fourteen hours and line fishing eight to ten hours. There are, of course, many devotees of shore angling and many of these regularly fish throughout the night.

R. E. Scott, Warden

10

DUNGENESS
Bird Observatory, Romney Marsh

At the time of the founding of the Folkestone Natural History Society, Dungeness was an exposed, isolated shingle headland. It was almost an island, for the tremendous expanse of shingle possessed no means of communication and lacked the present-day developments that have opened the area to the public. To reach anywhere it was necessary to walk several miles, many of them over the pebble beach, and the Dungeness fishing community had little if any connection with the outside world.

Within this haven were vast colonies of nesting sea-birds, mainly the black-headed gulls or *crockers* as the local fishermen called them, and also the common tern. Accurate counts of the numbers breeding in the nineteenth century are lacking and indeed they may even have been impossible to ascertain, but descriptions such as 'thousands' and 'the colony one mile long by 200 yards wide' appear in the early literature.

The area was considered of such importance for nesting sea-birds that in 1907 the Royal Society for the Protection of Birds employed a watcher or warden in the area and by 1929 the first purchase of land was made in the hope of preserving the natural history and scientific interest of the area. By 1936 the present reserve of 1,200 acres was under the management of the RSPB.

The first major change at Dungeness occurred during the Second World War when the entire area was requisitioned as part of the national defence plan. Mines were laid and the entire area was turned into ranges for the training of the war-time machine. This, coupled with the food shortage and the resultant gathering of sea-bird eggs for human consumption all but exterminated the colonies. In 1952 when the natural history movement was once more under-way the black-headed gulls which once nested in their thousands were down to two pairs, while the common terns whose colony once stretched for a mile along the beach could only muster twenty-six pairs.

It was in 1952 that the present ornithological organization at Dungeness came into being. Since then there has been more develop-ment, encroachment and destruction in the shingle areas. The need has grown to preserve at least some of Dungeness for the wildlife, where it can live as it did in the past while being studied, in the hope that the position may be improved in the future.

Thanks to the work of a variety of bodies including the Nature Conservancy, the Royal Society for the Protection of Birds, the Kent Ornithological Society, the London Natural History Society and the Hastings & East Sussex Natural History Society, it was possible to appoint a full-time warden at the RSPB Reserve in 1952, and in the same year to open the Dungeness Bird Observatory. Since then, the breeding birds and the passage migrants have been studied annually, apart from a partial gap in 1959 as a result of the uncertainty caused by the proposed Nuclear Power Station on the southern shore at Dungeness.

DUNGENESS BIRD RESERVE

The large sea-bird colonies had been lost, but Dungeness was still the only English breeding station for the common gull. It still holds its scattering of pairs of the local stone curlew. The little terns, although decreasing throughout the country still breed in fair numbers along the shore line and species such as the wheatear, little owl and kestrel are still annual breeders. The wheatear population has been substantially increased by the provision of artificial nesting boxes which are readily used, and the long-eared owl has been found as a regular nesting species. Even the decreased common tern and black-headed gull are on the increase once more. One of the major developments at Dungeness has been the increase and expan-sion of gravel diggings, the excavation of shingle for commercial purposes. This has resulted in many water areas, several of them with islands. On these the terns and gulls have found safe nesting sites, safe from human disturbance and the ground predators that so readily take their eggs.

Dungeness is likely to see many more changes in the years to come, but thanks to the efforts of the Royal Society for the Protection of Birds and the many friends of Dungeness, the position of many of the breeding birds is now assured.

DUNGENESS BIRD OBSERVATORY

The generosity of G. T. Paine enabled the Observatory to operate upon part of the Dungeness estate, and the annual collection of information relating to bird migration has continued since 1952. The Observatory is operated by an independent committee, which co-operates with other observatories through the offices of the British Trust for Ornithology.

Birds will continue to migrate whatever developments man makes, and as a result the many changes at Dungeness have had little effect on the migration work, although human pressure on the area certainly hampers operations at certain times of the year.

At the end of 1966 the Observatory had trapped, ringed and released over 84,000 birds of 167 species and this has thrown tremendous light on migratory movements. Subsequent recoveries of ringed birds have included starlings from Russia, wheatear from Iceland, wren from France, blackbird from Finland and Spain, and common terns from the east coast of Equatorial Africa. In addition to the ringing activities the Observatory's daily census records have provided information on the times of movements and the numbers involved, while other work has covered a range of subjects including moult, parasites, length of life, plumage characters, effects of lighthouses, etc.

As with the bird reserve, the support for the Observatory and its work is such that its future is assured.

Dorothy Long NDD

11

BOTANY

in and around Denton

The Denton valley, which runs roughly north-west to south-east has pure chalk nearly to the surface on the easternmost slopes, while on the west side there is clay-with-flints to a varying depth. On the top plateaux there is clay-with-flints in some places to a depth of fourteen feet. Recent geological surveys have shown firm, white, massively bedded chalk with black flint nodules at Lodgeleas in one spot and clay at another not far away. South-west of Walderchain Wood clay-with-flints is overlain by patches of brick-earth. A pit at Denton Court shows about fifteen feet of chalk while not far from Wootton Church the chalk is overlain by one foot of brown flinty clay beneath two to three feet of flinty loam. North of Wootton Church the chalk is capped by one foot of chocolate-brown clay below two and a half feet of brick-earth and east of this four feet of flinty brick-earth is exposed. (See *The Geological Survey of the area around Canterbury & Folkestone*. HMSO.)

The climate is practically maritime as no part of East Kent is directly more than nine miles from the sea, and this in three directions. Exposure to north-east winds usually keeps plant growth back in spring and some of the valley bottoms create frost pockets where sheltered from the sea winds.

Denton appears to have almost a micro-climate for records kept during the past nine years show a consistently higher rainfall than for the surrounding towns. The highest for Denton was in 1966 when it amounted to 50·18 inches and the lowest in 1962 when it was

31·30 inches. In 1966 Folkestone received 39·30 inches, Dover 44·49 inches and Ramsgate 38·34 inches. 1966 was exceptionally wet but the figures for other years show the same relative differences. Wild flowers seem more prolific after a wet than after a very dry year, though seed setting and fertilization may be poorer.

Modern methods of farming involving the grubbing of hedges and shelter belts, the bulldozing and ploughing of woodlands, crop spraying and modern field drainage, are having an enormous effect on our flora; while the increasing pressures on the use of land are causing losses every day. To give but two recent examples, the round-leaved winter-green *Pyrola rotundifolia* was recently destroyed near Elham in one of its only four stations in East Kent, by grubbing and ploughing of scrub, and one of two stations for the narrow-lipped helleborine *Epipactis leptochila*, was lost when Woolwich Wood was bulldozed and ploughed. This was in spite of great efforts to save it by the Kent Trust for Nature Conservation, the Committee for Preservation of Rural Kent, many local residents, and after two Public Inquiries. More and more land is needed for building, industry, and colliery spoil, and more and more water is taken from the rivers.

One more hazard noticed during the last few months is the new type of machine used for cutting roadside verges which slices the herbage in many places right to the bare earth.

On open chalk banks in Denton Parish are many orchids, namely man, green-veined, musk, pyramidal, common spotted and bee. Other plants growing on the chalk banks are rock rose, autumn gentian *Gentianella amarella*, centaury, blackstonia, chalk milkwort, squinancy wort and the large wild thyme *Thymus pulegioides*. This is easily recognized by its nearly square stem with two convex and two concave sides and hairs concentrated on the four ridges. In the scrub is our handsome lady orchid now found only in Kent.

Many of the woods left to us are typical chestnut and hazel coppice with oak and/or chestnut standards. These are gradually being replaced by highwood or coppice alone where conifers have not already been planted. The coppice with standards produces wonderful crops of primroses the year after the coppice is cut, when the light shade of the standards is ideal for these plants and many others such as the two kinds of dog violets, also hairy violet, three-nerved sandwort *Moehringia trinervia* and wood sorrel, all plants which finish their blooming before the shade becomes too dense. Bluebells are plentiful and seem to be able to tolerate more shade and many of the woods

Fly Orchid (*left*) and Lady Orchid.

are carpeted. Later on these woods produce herb paris, common,
hairy, slender and trailing St John's wort, orpine *Sedum telephium*, and

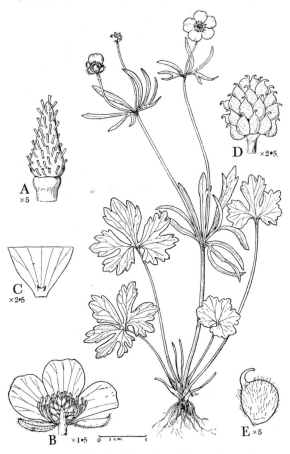

Goldilocks or Woodland Buttercup *Ranunculus auricomus*.
A. receptacle; B. flower; C. petal with nectary;
D. head of achenes; E. achene.

lesser periwinkle, and in one or two, columbine, though the best
wooded bank for this in the Covet Wood has been cut and re-
afforested with conifers by the Forestry Commission; also toothwort,
parasitic on hazel, wood betony, and bitter vetch; and on clay,
devil's bit scabious, great woodruff *Luzula sylvatica* and goldilocks,
the woodland buttercup which sometimes has its full complement of
five petals, sometimes one or two, and at other times none. One of
our more uncommon plants which grows in three or four local woods,
is common solomon's seal.

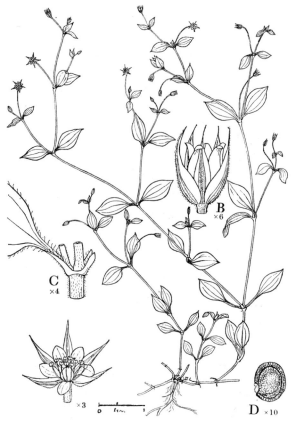

Three-nerved Sandwort *Moehringia trinervia*.
A. flower; B. capsule; C. node; D. seed.

In the Walderchain Wood a patch of tuberous comfrey has appeared among the small conifers grown for Christmas trees, probably imported with seedlings from Scotland. Foxglove, a chalk hater, does not grow nearer than Acrise. The dense shade of a typical beechwood on chalk, limits the number of plants, but the fly orchid, large white helleborine *Cephalanthera damasonium*, and bird's nest orchid can be found in three woods in the area; also spurge laurel *Daphne laureola* with its yellowish green, fragrant flowers, and butcher's broom with bright red berries in the autumn. Orchids, lilies of the valley, and primroses are unfortunately often dug up by the roots and sold in little baskets made of hazel twigs. Green hellebore grows in one or two woods, and sweet woodruff with a scent like new-mown hay. Sanicle carpets some of the beechwoods.

Some other interesting plants growing in the open, mainly on chalk or sand, are the broomrapes, including the tall broomrape *Orobanche elatior*, parasitic on knapweed, the great broomrape *O. rapum-genistae*, parasitic on broom and gorse, the clove-scented *O. caryophyllacea* nearer the sea parasitic on bed straw, and the rarest, the purple broomrape *O. purpurea* parasitic on yarrow.

In the arable fields two poppies are to be found in addition to the field poppy, namely the pale poppy and the bristle-headed, the latter being uncommon. The small fumitory *Fumaria parviflora* with white flowers, occurs in some fields as also the venus looking-glass or corn campanula, but the rarest is the ground pine *Ajuga chamaepitys* growing near Fredville where it has been known in the same field for over seventy years. This, one of only two stations in East Kent, is a chalky arable field which seems to have escaped spraying. The ground pine here is very much smaller than in West Kent, only reaching about two inches in height. Other plants growing in the same field include dwarf spurge, field woundwort, both fluellins and a rare knotgrass *Polygonum rurivagum*.

The lovely viper's bugloss with its brillaint blue flowers grows plentifully in some chalk fields as well as some of the shrubs and trees so typical of the chalk, such as spindle, wayfaring, guelder rose, dogwood and whitebeam. Barberry, which grew in one place in Denton for at least fifty years was unfortunately cut down recently but, as it has not been grubbed, there is hope it may grow again. This shrub was found to harbour the rust disease of wheat and so most plants have since been eradicated.

In conclusion one must mention the new East Kent discovery, the pale St John's wort *Hypericum montanum* about two and a half miles from Denton in typical chalk scrub. It is a very much smaller plant here than in western England, for example in the Forest of Dean, and it has probably reached the eastern limit of its range in East Kent.

It has been impossible in these notes to give anything like a complete list of the plants in the area, but in trying to give a balanced picture mention has been made of the rare, the uncommon or local, the common and the beautiful. Beauty and rarity do not always go together and sometimes beauty lies more in the eye of the beholder.

J. C. Harrison,
District Officer, Forestry Commission

12

LYMINGE BEAT
Part of Challock Forest

POLICY AND OBJECTS OF MANAGEMENT

Lyminge Beat, near Folkestone, which is part of Challock Forest, is owned and managed by the Forestry Commission, whose general policy can be summed up as follows:

To increase the production of wood as a raw material for industry by extending the area of its forests at a steady rate, in accordance with sound land use; and by making each forest as productive as possible.

Within the limits set by its other objectives to manage the forest estate as profitably as possible.

To provide employment in rural areas, especially those most affected by depopulation, and in so doing to maintain a skilled labour force.

To help in maintaining an efficient home timber trade.

To give due attention to the aesthetic and protective roles of the forest and to encourage open-air recreation.

To foster industrial and social development ancillary to forestry.

The objects of management of Challock Forest as a whole are:

To establish and maintain a forest of both conifers and hardwoods, primarily for the production of high-quality saw timber.

To maintain an even-aged stand structure for all crops.

To establish hardwoods only on sites of exceptionally high fertility or on sites not suited to conifers.

To grow such hardwood crops to produce high-quality saw logs of 16 to 18 inches mid quarter girth, 20 feet in length as quickly as possible. It is anticipated that this will be achieved in a mean rotation of approximately one hundred and five years.

To grow conifer crops to produce high-quality saw logs of 12 to 14 inches mid quarter girth, twenty feet in length. It is anticipated that this will be achieved in a mean rotation of approximately fifty-five years in the case of douglas fir, norway spruce and corsican pine, and sixty years in the case of scots pine.

To maintain and improve existing chestnut coppice only where high quality justifies its retention, and to manage it as one felling series.

To produce from the thinnings removed under the policy of moderately heavy thinning necessary for the achievement of the above objects: pitprops, pulpwood, and such other materials as will result in the most profitable utilization.

To market for pitwood, pulpwood, or rough timber, crops which will not produce high-quality saw logs.

To establish in due course separate hardwood and conifer high forest felling series; but meantime to achieve a balanced age class distribution in a single high forest felling series.

To dispose of all produce wherever possible by means of standing sales to the established trade but otherwise to maintain a permanent skilled labour force sufficient to meet the long-term requirement of the working plan.

To pay due regard to amenity and the maintenance and improvement of soil fertility.

To manage the non-forest portions of the estate as behoves a good landlord.

HISTORY

The Lyminge Beat area is now 2,653 acres in extent and consists of the following blocks with their acreages:

	West Wood, Park Wood and
1,202	*Elham Park Wood*
607	*Covert and Covet Woods*
764	*Denge Wood*
80	*Brook and Cadman's Woods*

2,653

The extensive forest which originally covered much of Kent had been cleared to quite a large extent by the Middle Ages. Until this time the main use of the forest had been for hunting and as a feeding ground for swine. By the late Mediaeval period the oak standards-with-coppice system had probably become established, and most of the Kentish woodlands were of this type. Chestnut coppice later became very valuable, and undoubtedly the original coppice species were replaced by chestnut to a large extent, this work mainly occurring in the late nineteenth century. In the early twentieth century, the larger proportion of the Kentish woodlands were therefore oak standards, mainly over coppice of various species — chestnut, ash, hornbeam, hazel, birch, maple and sallow. The chestnut areas were usually regularly cut as coppice. Although the demand for hop-poles had decreased, owing to a wire-frame method of hop growing, there was an increasing demand for chestnut for fencing material. There was little demand for the other species of coppice, which were seldom cut regularly, and were generally overgrown.

Rehabilitation of the woodland was normally beyond the means of the owner so, after the Forestry Commission was formed, such land was often taken over by it.

The Forestry Commission was established in 1919 and, in Kent, subsequently took over the Crown forest of Bedgebury. Then followed the acquisition of Covert and Covet Woods and Elham Park Woods from the Broome Estate, which was completed in 1925. Elham Park Wood is mentioned by Hasted in 1798 as belonging to the Lord of Elham Manor. The West Wood and Park Wood areas were also acquired in the same year from the Erle-Drax family. West Wood is mentioned by Hasted in 1798. He stated it was exchanged by Archbishop Cranmer with King Henry VIII in his thirty-first year. It then became part of the Manor of Lyminge. In 1798 it was in the ownership of Mr Sawbridge of Olantigh Estate. Hasted described the area as 'rough grounds covered with woods, scrubby coppice, broom and the like. Soil, unfertile red earth, intermixed with quantities of flint'. He also described the inhabitants as being as rough as the place, although we hope we have improved since. Later, in 1870, Furley stated that Mr Drax was the owner. Denge Wood was mainly acquired by the Commission in 1932 from the Wentworth estates.

DESCRIPTION

As stated, much of the Lyminge woodland was of poor oak standards with coppice of birch, chestnut, oak, hazel with ash and hornbeam in places. As chestnut coppice was the only species of much value, it has been Forestry Commission policy from the early times to retain the good chestnut areas and replace the other coppice areas with High Forest species. The high forest species planted have been mainly the trees of the greatest timber value, best suited to the particular site. Timber value is not always easy to estimate, for foresters are always planning twenty years and more into the future, when timber values may be very different from what they are now, due to changing demands.

Thus in the early days at Lyminge, from 1926 to 1935, the main tree species planted were european larch and douglas fir. Much of the european larch has been felled in recent years but the douglas fir is still thriving, and the main plantations are quite conspicuous as they adjoin Stone Street (County road B2068).

These early plantations did not look too healthy at the start and indeed the larch never really thrived, and gradually a preference was shown for beech. This phase lasted for practically fifteen years, from 1936 to 1950, and accounts for most of the pure beech planting at Lyminge, although a small percentage of conifers was planted at the same time, much of which was scots pine.

In latter years there has been a swing away from broadleaved planting towards conifers. We now know much more about the economics of forestry and the traditional broadleaves (oak and beech) show up unfavourably against the quicker-growing conifers. As stated in the objects of management, broadleaves are planted on sites of exceptionally high fertility, which are few, or on sites not suited to conifers, such as chalk areas, or on areas where amenity is important.

The main site-type at Lyminge is the clay-with-flints, with the minor type of the chalk, which occurs mainly on slopes where the overlying clay-with-flints deposits have been eroded.

The clay-with-flints type is sub-divided into: a. clay loam, b. sandy loam, and c. heather present.

On type a. our economic choice is norway spruce with other possibilities in economic order: japanese larch, hybrid larch, western hemlock, beech, oak.

On type b. our choice is douglas fir with other possibilities: norway spruce, corsican pine, japanese larch, hybrid larch, western hemlock, beech and oak.

On type c. corsican pine and scots pine.

On the chalk the choice of tree species is very limited, and we favour beech or thuya plicata; also norway maple, lime, norway spruce and lawson cypress.

The modern practice is to mix broadleaved plantings with conifers to provide a quicker intermediate financial return and this is usually done in a three row/three row pattern.

Much of the conifer planting is pure but mixtures are used, especially with western hemlock and this species is often grown with douglas fir or corsican pine or norway spruce.

The existing areas and the acreages (1967) of the various tree species at Lyminge are as follows:

310	*pines (scots and corsican)*
250	*larches (european, japanese & hybrid)*
320	*spruces (mainly norway)*
650	*douglas fir*
50	*western hemlock*
20	*other conifers*
560	*beech*
30	*other broadleaves*
310	*sweet chestnut coppice*

2,500

6

The age class structure of the high forest trees is shown in the following table:

PY	CHF	BHF	*totals*
1961–66	470	60	530
1956–60	257	50	307
1951–55	165	117	282
1946–50	190	123	313
1941–45	4	68	72
1936–40	108	161	269
1931–35	140	44	184
1926–30	230	3	233
totals	1,564	626	2,190

PY—*planting year;* CHF—*conifer high forest;* BHF—*broadleaf high forest*

PRODUCTION

At Lyminge a certain amount of saleable produce in the chestnut areas was inherited. Coppice takes about fifteen years to mature, when a sale can be made. The recent average standing sale price has been £60 per acre, and the coppice material has been converted to hop-poles and fencing material. The coppice is constantly improved by planting up and layering in the gaps, and it is expected that the real price will improve in the future.

Thinning of the early conifer plantations began in 1949 and thinnings and fellings have increased since that date to an average of 80,000 cubic feet a year. This should increase to a steady maximum of about 250,000 cubic feet of timber per annum.

It should be noted that the average conifer crop at Lyminge gives one hundred and fifty cubic feet per acre per annum average over its lifetime, and beech eighty cubic feet per acre per annum. This is in the order of five tons and three tons of timber per acre per annum.

Most of the produce has so far been utilized for pit props and pulpwood; in the future the main markets are expected to be pulpwood and saw timber.

RISKS AND WILD LIFE

The art of the forester is to minimize risks by planting a healthy tree on the correct site. The rabbit is the number one enemy to young trees, and it is normally essential to fence new plantations against them. Hares do occasionally damage but cannot be termed a major pest. Grey squirrels are a very serious pest, because they strip the bark of pole crop broadleaf trees such as beech and sycamore. Constant control by shooting and trapping is necessary.

Voles, of course, abound. Occasional small areas show serious damage which coincides with the periodic rise in population. The short-tailed vole is one offender which causes damage to both conifers and broadleaves by gnawing bark at the root collar. The bank vole has caused more trouble by gnawing bark of both stem and branches up to six or seven feet above ground level, particularly of beech. No artificial control is considered economic.

There is co-operation with neighbouring farmers to control foxes. Badgers are considered friends of the forester, and special gates are constructed in rabbit fences to enable Brock to move freely along his runs. Apart from the occasional stray in Denge Wood, there are no deer at Lyminge, although there are black fallow in the King's Wood, Challock, area some eight miles away.

The species Man is sometimes an enemy—that is when it causes fire and wipes out the work of years in a few hours. Continual vigilance is required against the starting of fires, particularly in the early spring, when the bracken is dead and often tinder-dry in the easterly winds. Public access is certain to increase with the demand for recreational facilities. Luckily the British public are becoming more forest minded. The Forestry Commission is always keen to increase this trend and forest walks and nature trails are being planned in many Forestry Commission areas. It is expected to initiate something on these lines at Lyminge this year (1967). Schools are encouraged to adopt forest plots, and a school forest has recently been started at Lyminge by a Folkestone school.

There is no record at Lyminge of birds doing damage to plantations, and foresters are practically united in claiming them as friends, particularly the insectivorous birds. The forest is becoming one of the few sanctuaries for bird life, and of the rarer birds, buzzards and hen harriers are occasionally reported at Lyminge.

Insect plagues often cause serious harm, but only minor occurrences are known at Lyminge. *Adelges viridis* has caused some damage on larch by feeding on the needles. *Adelges cooleyi* on douglas fir has caused similar damage. The large pine weevil *Hylobius abietis* is ever-present and, if care is not taken, can severely bark young plantations. The pine sawfly, the larch leaf-miner and the felted beech coccus have all caused damage.

Of fungi, *Fomes annosus* is always potentially dangerous, and infection of the trees by spores is prevented by chemically treating freshly-cut conifer tree stumps. Honey fungus *Armillaria mellea* periodically attacks occasional conifers but is difficult to combat economically, apart from care in the choice of species. *Rhizina undulata* is always a risk as a root disease and colonizes the sites of fires, which have to be strictly limited.

Competing vegetation can be termed almost a risk, although a rich and varied growth is a sign of a good tree site. Honeysuckle and clematis are particularly luxuriant in places at Lyminge and can smother young plantations if not periodically cut back severely. Many foresters are keen botanists and we all like to see a varied vegetation. Rare orchids occur in places, also beds of lily of the valley. Care will be taken not to lose rare species under a heavy conifer canopy.

THE FUTURE

It is interesting to speculate on the future of Lyminge Beat. Many people deprecate the alteration of the Kentish scene by the planting of conifers. Unfortunately the traditional Kentish woodland of oak standards over coppice is no longer economic except in some particular areas. English oak is a fine timber, but the modern demand is small apart from the very best tree. Oak thinnings and even the final crop trees are seldom sold at an economic price, and, until the demand increases, the forester will seldom plant it except on the best sites and for mainly sentimental reasons. Give him an increasing market and he will plant and naturally regenerate this very fine native tree with enthusiasm.

Beech is the broadleaf best suited to Lyminge and certainly some fine lofty beech woods can be expected in the future, especially along wood margins and public roads. Sweet chestnut coppice areas will also make an important contribution to the crop in the traditional manner, to provide attractive pockets in the surrounding high forest. Meanwhile the forester's main bread and butter will be provided by european conifers — the pines, probably mainly corsican, and norway spruce; and by those fine western american trees, douglas fir and western hemlock.

Lyminge Forest will undoubtedly provide an increasing asset to the visual amenity of the country. It will also provide a permanent home for wild life. It will also provide a sound economic contribution to the countryside.

E. Hammond BSc

13

WYE & CRUNDALE DOWNS
National Nature Reserve

The Reserve is the most easterly of the country's national nature reserves on the chalk and covers two hundred and fifty acres of the steep scarp of the North Downs to the south of the Stour Gap at Wye. The Nature Conservancy's main purpose here is to conserve an example of the now rapidly disappearing chalk downland of East Kent, which is exceptionally rich in numbers and species of plants and insects.

In clear weather the views from the top of the Broad Downs are among the best in Kent and attract considerable interest. So that visitors can enjoy these views and see into the impressive dry valley or coombe known as the Devil's Kneadingtrough, access without permits is allowed on parts of Broad Downs as shown on the main sign boards and Reserve leaflets. But a permit is required for access to all other parts, except public rights of way and nature trails.

TOPOGRAPHY
The scarp face is unusual, being fretted by a cluster of large coombes, the best known and most spectacular of which is the Devil's Kneadingtrough with its prominent terracettes. The sides of these coombes are very steep, up to thirty-five degrees, and extend from under three hundred feet above sea-level at the valley bottom to over five hundred feet at the top. There are springs at intervals along the base of the scarp face, just above the junction of the Chloritic Marl with the Gault Clay which lies roughly on the two-hundred-foot contour.

The geology is relatively simple with the Chlorotic Marl present at the base of the Reserve overlain by Lower and Middle Chalk. The top of the escarpment is capped by a layer of clay-with-flints of varying thickness, and the plateau-like surface on top of the Downs, mostly outside the Reserve, is referable to the six-hundred-foot Pliocene erosion surface. Drift includes deposits in the bottoms of the coombes, down-washed chalk loam and other widespread superficial material resulting from sub-aerial erosion.

EARLY HISTORY

Geomorphological research by Kerney, Brown and Chandler in 1964 gives the latest evidence on the formation of the coombes. This indicates that they were formed under annual permafrost conditions within the remarkably short period of five hundred years, i.e. 8800–8300 BC, but there was no evidence that springs ever emerged at a higher level than they do today. Intensive study yielded evidence of Late and Post-glacial history of floral and faunal changes as well as man's influence on the area. The earliest deposits are marsh deposits of the Late Glacial period (10000–8800 BC) and the molluscan and plant, mostly pollen, evidence gives a fairly detailed picture. Post-glacial hillwash deposits contain a rich molluscan fauna, though oxidization has destroyed the pollen, while subsequent marsh deposits near the Reserve have yielded fauna of considerable zoo/geographical interest.

Man's influence is indicated by two clearance phases, the first possibly during the Beaker Period, late Neolithic to earliest Bronze Age, when the woodland species were largely replaced by grassland species. The second probably occurred in the Iron Age 'A' times with the onset of intensive arable farming. Pottery ranging from Iron Age to Romano-British ware has been found in the hillwashed chalk muds. The valley floor of the Devil's Kneadingtrough is thought not to have been ploughed until the later stages of the Roman era.

There are many features of archaeological interest such as ancient field systems, earthworks, tumuli and sunken trackways. Two presumed barrows at Broad Downs have been designated as Ancient Monuments by the Ministry of Public Buildings and Works.

In a preliminary survey of the earthworks in 1964 Wood and Bowen suggested that the strip lynchets are mediaeval and represent the temporary or sporadic extension of cultivation on the Downs,

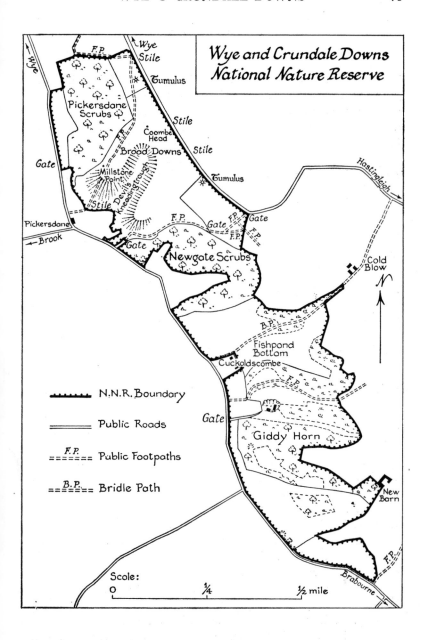

Wye and Crundale Downs
National Nature Reserve

Wye Stile
F.P.
Tumulus
Pickersdane Scrubs
Stile
Coombe Head
Brood Downs
Stile
F.P.
Gate
Millstone Point
Tumulus
Hastingleigh
Devil's Kneadingtrough
Stile
Pickersdane
Brook
F.P.
Gate
F.P.
Gate
F.P.
Gate
Newgate Scrubs
Cold Blow
N
B.P.
Fishpond Bottom
Cuckoldscombe
F.P.
Gate
Giddy Horn
New Barn
······ N.N.R. Boundary

——— Public Roads

=====F.P.===== Public Footpaths

=====B.P.===== Bridle Path

F.P.
Brabourne

Scale:
0   ¼   ½ mile

while linear hollows on the north-east corner of the Reserve are probably old drove ways or pack-horse routes.

SOILS

The soils are now being fully surveyed, but can be divided into three general categories: a. *Brown earths*, which tend to be atypical because of their greater acidity. These are found on the plateau, roughly above the five-hundred-foot contour. b. *Rendzinas*, on the steep scarp face. c. *Brown calcareous soils* at the base of the scarp face.

In the bottom of the Devil's Kneadingtrough a buried soil is revealed in section on the wall of the pit which was the shield for the firing range.

FLORA

Three habitat types, i.e. grassland, woodland and scrub are found on all the soil types, reflecting man's management of the area as opposed to natural plant/soil associations. During the 1950s and before the purchase of the Reserve almost all the level land was ploughed and re-seeded so that today over half the grassland is atypical of a chalk sward. It consists predominantly of a rye/clover mixture with white bent *Agrostis stolonifera* and cocksfoot *Dactylis glomerata*. Fortunately the re-seeding was not very successful on the thinner chalk soils and it resulted in a fairly high proportion of typical chalkland plants such as red and sheep's fescue *Festuca rubra* and *ovina*, rockrose *Heliathemum chamaecistus*, horseshoe vetch *Hippocrepis comosa*, large wild thyme *Thymus pulegioides*, marjoram *Origanum vulgare*, dwarf or stemless thistle *Cirsium acaulon* and cowslip *Primula veris*.

The steeper slopes escaped the plough and since the rabbit population was decimated by myxomatosis in 1954 they have become dominated by a dense blanket of tor grass *Brachypodium pinnatum* except for small areas of very shallow rendzina soils. Tor grass is not very palatable to stock and if ungrazed produces copious leaf litter which resists decay. This tends to eliminate or reduce certain typical constituents of the chalk sward while also acting as a nurse for scrub and bramble. This has given rise to a difficult management problem on which research is being done.

Most of the woodland is on the steep slopes of the coombes and has suffered only slight reduction since the beginning of the present century. It is predominantly ash with an understorey of hazel coppice, but there is also one small planted beech wood. Other notable tree species include whitebeam and yew with occasional oak, field maple, hornbeam and holly. The herb layer is dominated by dog's mercury *Mercuralis perennis* with herb paris *Paris quadrifolia*, bluebell *Hyacinthoides non-scripta* and ramsons garlic *Allium ursinum* locally abundant. Primrose *Primula vulgaris* occurs on most woodland margins and under the more open canopy conditions, while a few plants of the false oxlip *Primula veris × vulgaris* occur in one area.

Since the advent of myxomatosis scrub has appeared on all the ungrazed grassland and on most woodland margins. Hawthorn, privet, hazel, ash and bramble are the major constituents with way-faring tree, spindle and birch being locally abundant. This habitat is favoured by warblers and other singing birds, especially the nightingale which nests regularly in the large scrub on the woodland margins.

Kent is famous for its variety of orchids and the Reserve is no exception with seventeen known species including three orchis and four ophrys species. Because of their beauty and rarity they receive much attention and interest while certain species, notably the lady orchid *Orchis purpurea*, have unfortunately been extensively picked and even totally removed in the past. Since the formation of the Reserve, intensive wardening and the placing of wire cages over the more obvious flowering spikes have virtually stopped this destruction.

FAUNA

The Reserve and the surrounding downland has for many years attracted considerable interest among entomologists. Indeed the late Dr A. M. Massee has described the area as one of the richest insect localities in England. The Nature Conservancy is extremely grateful to Col C. A. W. Duffield for providing detailed records of invertebrates which represent the results of over forty years' work in the area.

It is not intended to discuss the entomology fully but mention must be made of representatives of two genera of Lepidoptera about which questions are frequently asked. Both the chalk hill blue *Lysandra coridon* and adonis blue *Lysandra bellargus* butterflies which formerly occurred on the Reserve have not been recorded in recent years. The burnet moths are well represented with strong colonies of the five spot *Zygaena trifolii* ssp. *palustrella*, the large or narrow-bordered five spot *Z. lonicerae* ssp. *transferens* and the six spot *Z. filipendulae*.

Owing to the relatively dry habitats and the absence of any

permanent body of water on the Reserve it is not surprising that amphibians occur only occasionally. By comparison the reptiles are well represented with the common lizard *Lacerta vivipara* and adder *Vipera berus berus* being locally numerous. Active badger setts exist in most of the woodland areas, although none are as extensive in size as those in Lyminge Forest and other localities. Most of the smaller native mammals occur and, while no detailed surveys have been undertaken to date, it is interesting to note a record for the dormouse in 1965, the first for the area in recent years.

Despite the large amount of deciduous woodland and scrub, the resident bird life is disappointingly poor and few migrants frequent the Reserve. A survey in 1955 listed only fifty-three species.

MANAGEMENT AND USE

The Reserve, like all other national nature reserves, is primarily managed to conserve its scientific interest and while other demands such as passive recreation are catered for, these must always be of secondary importance.

Since 1964 it has been possible to allow visitors on some parts of the Reserve so that they can enjoy the views. An increasing number of school parties have also been able to do field studies without damaging the flora and fauna. This policy of providing facilities for different interests has been successful mainly because a team of honorary voluntary wardens have assisted the Warden Naturalist and Part-time Warden in safeguarding the Reserve. These honorary wardens are also helping with important wildlife recording and scientific studies.

In the short time during which the Reserve has been in existence (1961) it has been the site of two important events. In May 1964 a party of Ashford Senior Scouts took part in a pilot scheme for a new syllabus for the Scout's Conservation Badge. It was largely as a result of the experience gained from this pilot course that the present method of testing has emerged.

In June and July 1966 nearly two thousand Kent schoolchildren took part in a field studies scheme jointly organized and run by the Kent Education Committee and the Nature Conservancy. It was the first time that many pupils had carried out field studies, and it has been generally agreed that the scheme gave the children a wider interest in the countryside.

By permission of 'The Times'

14

ROMNEY MARSH
its Subtle and Changing Beauty

'The world according to the best geographers is divided into Europe, Asia, Africa, America and Romney Marsh.' People living on Romney Marsh did not find this statement from the Rev R. H. Barham's *Ingoldsby Legends* in any way outrageous. It was no more than they were already aware of.

There are other marsh pastures, but Romney Marsh is unique by virtue of its geographical position, its strange geology, its unusual flowers and birds, its little towns, villages, and extraordinarily large number of lovely churches, and a haunting though undramatic beauty. When you stand upon its levels you feel none of the monotony which extensive flatness usually conveys. This is because your eye, travelling over the flats, always reaches distant hills. You are never out of sight of hills. They form a half-circle round the Marsh, and beyond is another land. The other way lies the sea.

Romney Marsh is not so much the name of a district as an all-embracing term. Romney Marsh itself comprises less than half the area which its name is loosely made to cover. The whole area runs to some 58,865 acres, of which Romney Marsh takes in about 24,000 acres. The rest is made up of Walland Marsh, Denge Marsh, the Rother Levels and various other levels; and you do not know when you have passed from one to another. Marshmen get over the difficulty by dubbing the whole lot comprehensively the Marsh.

Marshmen who lived like Barham in the eighteenth century were very like their country—withdrawn and insular, and suspicious when visited by 'foreigners', which meant anybody not a marshman. To some extent this is still true today, but things are changing. Until the Second World War the Marsh was predominantly grass, supporting great flocks of sheep and big herds of beef cattle. It was a wonderful sight, and it turned even the prosaic Cobbett lyrical. 'The flocks and herds immense', he noted in *Rural Rides*. 'The sheep are of a breed that takes its name from the Marsh. . . . Very pretty and large. . . . The cattle appear to be all of the Sussex breed. Red, loose-limbed, and, they say, a great deal better than the Devonshire.'

Wartime demands meant more arable crops. The plough bit into the rich and ancient pastures, and marshmen prophesied crop disaster through drowning, since the Marsh was subject to flooding, and anyway was always more than a little damp, to say the least. They were wrong. Great crops of corn and roots ensued. Marsh farmers stubbornly continued to detest the change, nevertheless: but worse was to come. 'Foreigners' arrived from Lincolnshire after the war, buying land, which was cheaper than the flat land of their own country, and generally more fertile; and they planted bulbs. Tulips and daffodils grew where the famous Romney Marsh sheep once grazed. Marshmen were scandalized.

The new pattern has endured. Today the Marsh is mixed arable and pasture. But the new farming has not banished the old beauty, the constantly changing quality of the sharply yellow light, the cloud shadows that slide down the hills, dapple the flat land and slide away over the sea, the willows and the reeds that grow beside the dykes.

The sea is an all-pervading presence, almost always to be seen and frequently heard. Sometimes, however, on calm, white days, when the sky is covered with thin translucent cloud, it becomes invisible to anybody standing a mile or so back from the shore. White horizon merges with white sky and there is no line of demarcation. On such days a stranger will rub his eyes in disbelief as a ship floats by apparently in the air.

The sea is often above you as you stand on the flats, particularly when the spring tides are running. Strong sea-walls have been built to keep it out, and these have become an integral part of the Marsh scene.

The hills which now enclose the Marsh are the remains of cliffs which once enclosed a great bay. The bay gradually silted up, creating the rich alluvial soil, but this did not happen in one gradual, progressive process. The sea has advanced and retreated, the land has risen and fallen, some half a dozen times in the past 12,000 years. Once a forest stood there. Primitive communities made their homes there. The sea came in and drowned the trees, retreated, and the bay became a morass of mud and tangled vegetation. All the time silt was building up from rivers, three in particular, the Rother, the Brede, and the Tillingham, all still there and still bringing down silt.

The strange ups and downs of the land, plus the drift of the tides, formed one of the most interesting geological phenomena in the country: the great shingle spit of Dungeness, still building up. But Dungeness is now better known for the atomic station standing there than for its natural significance.

The Marsh today is suffering from a depression, one which set in about 1,500 years ago, although by that time man had begun to take a strong controlling hand. The Romans put their engineering skill to work and built a sea-wall. The Church from Canterbury instituted well-thought-out drainage and protection schemes. Archbishop Becket started a grand scheme which eventually led to the reclamation of the whole Marsh. As the sea was pushed back so the silt built up and presently even the towns and villages that developed along the extensive estuaries, inlets and rivers were left high and dry, including the famous Cinque Ports of Rye and Winchelsea. These two towns now wear a mellow air of permanent retirement which crowds of summer tourists do nothing to dispel.

In the course of time the Marsh became the most famous grazing ground in the world. The forest was no more than a hazy legend, only half-believed. But the big mechanical implements of modern agriculture and drainage have brought it to mind, if not to life. The great ploughs, ditchers and dredgers cut through the silt like butter, but occasionally they are jarred to a standstill. Workers in the early days of deep cultivation were constantly surprised when this happened, but today's drivers know well enough what holds them up. They have struck a tree trunk, and it has to be dug out. Once on the surface there they lie on the rich earth, massive, black as ebony, hard as rock, mute reminders of those far-off days when man stood uncertainly on the threshold of civilized life. Marshmen call them moor oaks.

There are many places from which to view, and feel, the subtle beauty of the Marsh. My personal preference is the road above Lympne towards Canterbury. Up there you see the great green and tawny 'bay' spread out below like a map, cut by brilliant lines of silver which are the dykes, dappled by the ever-changing pattern of light and shadow.

But you often feel more when you see less. Of all the many hours I have spent on the Marsh, I remember best a calm, clear evening in late autumn. I stood on the sea-wall, just above the high tide. A fading pink and saffron sky tinted the water with its reflection, the reaches of the Marsh stretched into the dusk, and in all that level world I could hear only the whisper of small breezes in the reeds, the soft lap of the water beneath my feet and the cry of a single curlew passing overhead.

Vera F. P. Day NDH

15

A HUNDRED YEARS
of Change

Many changes may be expected over a period of a hundred years, but probably there have been more in the last fifty years than at any other time in our history.

Socially, the enormous increase in population since the Industrial Revolution brought many problems, not the least being the need for housing. Several major building schemes, with all these imply, took place between 1880 and the present day, the first at the turn of the century, the next after the 1914–18 war, and again after the 1939–45 war and still in progress, the result being that many rural areas became urban, with the consequent loss of wild life in these and near-by areas. Airfields and army training areas have sterilized large tracts throughout the country.

The invention of the petrol engine has affected all branches of human activity. Regions hitherto almost inaccessible have been opened up. Vast improvements in technology and mechanization, notably in agriculture, have changed the appearance of the land.

Mechanized farming, saving both time and labour, has resulted in the depopulation of villages. Far more land is under cultivation. Hedges have been grubbed, spinneys cleared and ponds filled in, all the natural habitat of many plants and animals. The reckless use of poisonous sprays, the effects sometimes being persistent and cumulative, has done much damage to wildlife and ruined many attractive banks and road verges. The ploughing of once permanent pastures has further altered the vegetation, causing such species as grassland orchids and cowslips, once abundant, to be classed as rare or becoming extinct. The reduction of sheep walks on the Downs has encouraged the growth of trees and bushes.

Rabbits have been directly responsible for major changes in the landscape. Reaching pest proportions in the '20s and '30s, they occupied poor and difficult land allowed to revert to coarse grass and brambles after the 1914 war effort. Here they kept down the scrub and coarse vegetation to a considerable extent. This was not realized until they were cleared wholesale by myxomatosis in the early '50s, for since their disappearance coarse grass and scrub have smothered many attractive small wild flowers, and reduced the numbers of butterflies, which have lost their food plants, and this rapid growth of invasive species has proved a difficult problem in maintaining rare species in nature reserves. Once bare Downs, too, are being covered with bushes.

Against these losses many alien plants, notably oxford ragwort and common buddleia, have become established in SE England, together with a number of birds hitherto only recorded as chance visitors. The collared dove, for example, now occurs in large flocks.

Further changes have occurred through wholesale drainage and increasing demand for water for household and industrial purposes, in some cases lowering the water table dangerously, and drying up ditches, streams and small lakes, with consequent effects on wildlife. Influx of sewage has destroyed fishes and much other aquatic life. The building of atomic power stations, on the other hand, has created several small unofficial nature reserves.

Forestry has brought about many changes, on the whole beneficial, increasing the number of birds and animals, and in some cases, plant life; in others conifers have suppressed the undergrowth, and with it the accompanying wildlife.

The reduction of footpaths through war-time neglect and increased cultivation has had to receive attention when recreation must be considered. The wholesale destruction of amenities by holiday makers in the country and along the coast has spoiled many beauty spots. Attempts to alleviate this are being made by the provision of holiday camps and planned caravan sites and car parks. To combat this violation of the countryside, and wholesale destruction of wild life, a number of societies and trusts have been formed in the last fifty years. The National Trust, the Royal Society for the Protection of Birds, the Fauna Preservation Society, the County Naturalists'

Trusts, World Wildlife Fund and others are helping to interest the public in conservation and are setting up nature reserves in many places to prevent wildlife from becoming depleted or extinct. In addition, the teaching of biology in all schools has aroused considerable interest in natural history among young people generally, and there is widespread appreciation of broadcast programmes by well-known naturalists.

Margery H. Walton

16

ON FOOT
through the District

THE WARREN
Starting point: East Cliff Pavilion (107 bus route)
Distance: by the sea-wall approximately 4 miles
by the cliff path approximately 5 miles

The Warren is a unique area some two miles in length, lying at the
foot of the massive chalk cliffs between Folkestone and Dover, and
extending from East Wear Bay to Abbot's Cliff.

The 107 bus terminus is outside the East Cliff Pavilion. On the
south side of this building lies Copt Point which is composed of
gault clay, a grey water-logged mass which is forever slipping seawards. Some interesting fossils can be found, especially in the lower
levels, notably ammonites which are often in beautiful condition.

It is easier to take the road along the left side of the Pavilion and
walk towards the martello towers, one on each side of the road.
These towers formed part of the coast defence scheme against
Napoleon, and the name is taken from Cape Mortella in Corsica.

The car park between the road and cliff edge covers the founda-
tions of a large Roman villa. This was fully excavated in 1924, but
was grassed down again after the Second World War. It is likely that
a prominent officer of the Classis Britannica, the Roman Fleet, lived
here during the third and fourth centuries after Christ, for it is
thought that a Roman road linking Dover with Lympne passed to the
northward of the area which is now Folkestone.

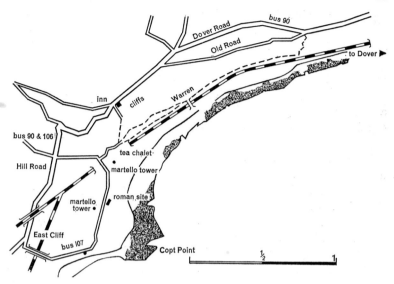

A road on the right enters the Warren near the last of the towers. British Rail own a new road on the seaward side of the line and this leads to a vast concrete apron on the foreshore which was constructed to give stability to the gault reefs which had been raised at low tide level by pressure from the mass of chalk which forms the cliffs. The most spectacular slip occurred in the winter of 1915–16 when the water which drained from the cliffs was trapped by the clay at the base, and the whole plastic mass slid forward. An extensive and costly system of drainage has been put in since then to safeguard the railway, but in spite of this considerable slipping has occurred. After the chalk has crumbled is a good time for fossil hunting, and near the concrete apron deposits of marcasite can still be found at low tide.

Two paths lead from the refreshment chalet which stands on a plateau above the railway cutting. One winds steeply down with steps cut in the slope, and follows a course close to the cliff face through an area of thick undergrowth, interesting alike to botanists and bird lovers. Dense bushes provide the common whitethroat and the turtle dove with the kind of shelter they like, and the lovely song of the blackcap can be heard even when the little bird is hard to see. On the rocks the black redstart may be seen in passage during spring and autumn. The other path runs down close to the railway, and both ways meet near the old Warren Halt which is no longer used by passengers; but there is a bridge over the line a few hundred yards further along to the eastward. This used to be a famous area for entomologists, but camping has spoilt it, though it must always be the first landfall for migrating insects from the Continent. Some rare species may still be caught under favourable circumstances. The clouded yellow *Colias croceus* come over in large numbers during a good year, together with a few large tortoiseshells *Nymphalis polychloros*. The fiery clearwing *Aegeria chrysidiformis* which is not a migrant, can be found here.

There are two ways back to the town, either over the bridge and along the sea-wall to Copt Point, or up the zig-zag cliff path which comes out on the Dover Road near the *Royal Oak*. All the way up there is a magnificent view out over the sea. At sunset the cliffs of France gleam white in the level rays, and at all hours of the day ships of many nations pass through the Channel on their lawful occasions.

The way back to Folkestone along the cliff top need not be entirely on the main road where there is a frequent bus service (number 90). By keeping to the cliff edge, along the old road, it is possible to get within a few hundred yards of the *Valiant Sailor*. Here on the left beside the inn there is a path which in summer is carpeted with harebells and wild thyme, and this leads down over the open hill-side to the last martello tower and the entrance to the Warren.

One can either go back to the 107 bus terminus which is clearly visible, or scramble down on to the road which leads into the Warren and turn right. This road goes past a housing estate to reach the main Dover Road opposite Hill Road. Buses 90 and 99 stop there.

NEWINGTON NEAR FOLKESTONE

Starting point: Killicks Corner on Dover Hill (Buses 90 or 99)
Distance: Killicks Corner to Newington approximately 5 miles
Type of walk: by-roads

Killicks Corner is the name given to the hairpin bend on Dover Hill (A259) just beyond the last houses and below the disused quarry where a burial ground, probably of jutish origin, was excavated soon after the First World War. This point can be reached on a 90 bus from Bouverie Square or 99 from the Town Hall. The stop is at Hill Road as Killicks Corner is too steep.

A little-used road branches out on the left, opposite a bungalow, and climbs slantwise up the chalk downs to reach Crete Road East.

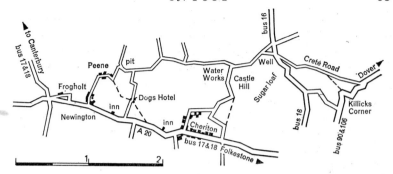

This is a second-class road which runs from the *Valiant Sailor* to join the main Canterbury road (A260) behind Sugar Loaf, a strange conical hill rising abruptly from the coastal plain of Folkestone. Between Sugar Loaf and Middle Hill, deep in an overgrown cleft is Holy Well, or St Thomas's Well as it is called in old documents. The spring is completely neglected now and little known even to Folkestone people, but it has been suggested that in the Middle Ages it was an important source of water for pilgrims and their pack animals, especially after the Shrine of St Thomas of Canterbury became an object of world-wide devotion.

After crossing the A260, which is a bus route between Folkestone and Canterbury (route 16) with a half-hourly service, the by-road continues westward to Caesar's Camp where it then goes under the name of Crete Road West. The Romans may have sited one of their beacons here, but it is considered that the earthworks belong to pre-history, and the traces of a watchtower to the time of Stephen and his mutinous barons. The long, deep scars just below the summit of these hills are tank traps from the last war. Some interesting plants grow here, including the horned poppy and the sea cabbage.

The oldest town reservoir can be seen from the road which leads steeply down to Cherry Garden Avenue. At the beginning of the century it was a place for family picnics amongst the fruit trees, but now the safety of public health demands that the area be enclosed by unclimbable wire fences. The woods behind the reservoirs are a sanctuary for birds and rare plants. Wild candytuft has colonized Chimney Hill and this is the only place where the plant grows in the South of England.

In winter visiting kestrels may be seen soaring over the high land, and autumn brings the fieldfares and redwings to winter here. The hoopoe is rare but may sometimes be found, chiefly on grass fields and lawns during the spring or autumn migration.

The bare hills provide the bright sunshine beloved by many butterflies, notably the grayling *Eumenis semele*, the marbled white *Melanargia galathea* and the lovely vivid chalk hill blue *Lysandra coriden*. Every stem of grass seems to support the little yellow cocoons of the six-spot burnet *Zygaena filipendulae* and the small brightly-coloured moths may be flying about in hundreds.

Crete Road West continues along the summit of the downs with panoramic views over Shorncliffe Camp towards the far-off hills at Fairlight near Hastings. At the roadside the great cotton thistle and many chalk-loving plants grow. About a mile beyond Casear's Camp the road forks and bends sharply down, one lane continuing along the foot of the hills to a lime quarry. Here another lane turns off to the left to reach Peene and Newington. In July the chalky banks are covered with wild orchids, especially with the pyramidal and scented varieties. The lane on the left, turning before the quarry, goes to the Dogs' Hotel, where there is a field path on the left to Cheriton.

There have been dwellings in Peene since Saxon times, and near by under Milky Down skeletons have been unearthed probably belonging to the Neolithic Period. Newington is only about a mile southward along a winding lane, and the village is charming, with a beautiful little church. If the walk is too long there is a short cut back to Cheriton from the housing estate at Peene over the fields past the Dogs' Hotel to join the other path from below the quarry.

St Nicholas's Church at Newington belongs to the twelfth century and contains no less than thirteen ancient brasses. Most of them have been moved from their original positions so that John Clerk, a Vicar who died in 1501, now has three children of Thomasine Chylton placed beside him. Thomas Chylton and his wife are remembered by a curious brass which shows the man in his shroud which has been left open to reveal his face.

The A20 with an hourly bus service runs very close to the church. There is, however, another interesting thing to see. A few hundred yards over the fields westwards from the church is Frogholt with a tiny thatched cottage bending over a stream. This is probably one of the earliest dwellings in SE England still in a state of repair, and the moss-covered banks of the lane produce violets and little spring flowers when the rest of the country is still in the grip of winter. The

A20 runs parallel to this lane and is only a short distance away, and where the lane joins the road at Beachborough Corner, bus 17 or 18 will stop on request. Cheriton and a frequent town bus service is only about a mile eastward along the main road. On the way refreshments can be obtained at the *Star Inn*.

LYMPNE & ROMNEY MARSH
Starting point : Hythe Light Railway Station (from Folkestone bus route 103a)
Distance : approximately 5 miles
Type of walk : by-roads and fields paths

The Royal Military Canal runs from Seabrook to Rye, and formed part of the coast defence against Napoleon's threatened invasion early in the last century. The walk from Hythe to West Hythe along either bank is very pleasant, for the canal is sheltered on the north by the long clay escarpment. After about a mile and a half West Hythe is reached. This was once an important port, and in Roman times there was a good anchorage in the estuary of the river Rother which ran along the foot of the hills until a series of great storms in the twelfth century blocked the river mouth with shingle and diverted the course to Rye.

On the north bank of the canal stands a ruined church dedicated

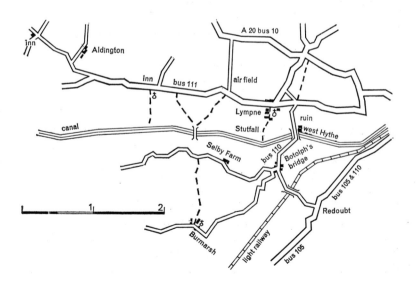

to Our Lady of West Hythe. The building was destroyed by fire three hundred years ago.

Just beyond the church a road bridge crosses the canal, and half a mile further on, still on the north bank, there is a stile and foot-bridge on the right nearly opposite the tower of Lympne Church, which stands out on the skyline. The path up the hillside is easily discernable, and it passes close to the great masses of stonework which mark the site of the roman fortress of Stutfall, or Portus Lemanis. The buildings once covered more than ten acres, but the hillside is composed of clay, constantly slipping, and over the centuries the massive walls fell, the stones were carried away and used by the Saxons and Normans, and grass grew over what remained. The site has never been fully excavated though some work was done here in the middle of the last century.

The path ends at the top of the escarpment beside Lympne Castle, a castle only in name, for the building fronting the road is a gracious manor house of the time of Henry V. It has been extensively altered and restored. On the south side there is a strong tower which could have been defended, and this probably stands on the site of a Roman watch-tower, from which the conquerors could see the Channel, and the building of the earliest wall at Dymchurch.

The great Norman tower of the church contains a good deal of roman material, possibly from Stutfall on the hillside below. It is believed that Archbishop Lanfranc was the builder of the original church, but the present chancel and north aisle belong to the thirteenth century.

From Lympne churchyard there is a magnificent view over Romney Marsh. The Romans saw a vast inland sea dotted with many islands and sandbanks, and their engineers must have started the work of reclaiming the land beyond the Rhee Wall, because roman pottery and coins have been unearthed at Dymchurch. This work was continued over the centuries. In many places the Marsh is ten feet below high tide level and some of the most fertile land in the world owes its continued safety to the massive bulk of Dymchurch Wall. From the days of the Saxons an exact and complicated code was worked out for the responsibility of repairing it, and of keeping the drainage dykes in order. Within the last few years dyke clearance has been carried out with mechanized equipment and this has involved the destruction of many of the water plants, especially the dainty mauve marsh mallow, the water plantain and reed mace.

There are a number of large and fascinating churches scattered over the area, probably built by the owners of wealthy manors during the Norman Period and the Middle Ages. New Romney, Lydd and Brookland stand on the coast road; Brenzett, Ivychurch and St. Mary's have signposted lanes leading to the hamlets where they stand. Walking over the Marsh is very difficult as the dykes can usually only be crossed by bridges, so what looks like a direct path may turn into a jigsaw puzzle for the walker; and in the clear air with few landmarks distances can be very deceptive.

The furthest-out point in the view southward is the atomic power station on Dungeness. The 105 bus goes from Folkestone to Lydd and there is another circular bus route out to the point during the summer. The Hythe & Dymchurch Light Railway (the smallest public railway in the world) also joins Hythe to Dungeness during the summer months.

Up to fifty years ago this great mass of shingle, which is steadily growing out towards France, was one of the loneliest places on the coast, and the most difficult of access. During the Second World War, however, a concrete road was laid down to reach Pluto, the submarine pipeline to France, and since then the whole area has been opened up and buildings have spread right up the east side of the promontory. Fortunately the Royal Society for the Protection of Birds has acquired quite a large area for a Bird Sanctuary, and it is to be hoped that the rare plants which grow on Dungeness will also find safety there. During the autumn the pied flycatcher may be seen on migration, together with the ring ouzel and whinchats who also cross in the spring. Merlins often spend the winter months along this coastline.

On the east side of the Lydd-Dungeness road there is now a large area for the storage and conservation of water, and this may be the salvation of such rare plants as the greater spearwort, jasione, nottingham catchfly and the parasitic dodder spreading on the prostrate brooms. From the point of view of a naturalist the construction of the power station together with the waterworks area and bird reserve are to be welcomed, otherwise the whole area, unique in England, may have disappeared under a sprawling mass of bungalows. As it is the marsh shield fern, adder's tongue and marsh cinquefoil continue to survive in the bird reserve, but the lovely sea pea and sea bindweed which used to be common on the shingle and sand above high water have been eradicated, as new building has mushroomed along the concrete coast road. All over Dungeness masses of valerian brighten the shingle and attract painted lady butterflies *Vanessa cardui* and the gatekeeper *Maniola tithonus*.

At the north-eastern corner of Lympne churchyard a field path starts, and this passes a wood to join Lympne Hill a short distance from the top. There is a bus service back to Hythe from the canal bridge (110) a few hundred yards down the road. But up the hill there is something else of interest. This is the Shepway Cross, a modern, beautifully carved cross which marks the place where it is thought the Court of Shepway was held from very early times to elect the Lord Warden of the Cinque Ports. The ditches here produce a fine crop of the great horsetail.

A second-class road (B2067) runs across the top of Lympne Hill. From this point there are three ways by which to return to Hythe. Level with the Cross is a field path going due north for nearly a mile to join the main road to Hythe a few hundred yards from the New Inn (bus route 10). There is also a lane branching north-westwards beyond the Cross which reaches B2068, a road which skirts the airfield, near the *County Members* inn, then passes the old manor house of Berwick, and comes out at the cross-roads at New Inn Green (bus route 10). Finally, it is quite pleasant to walk all the way back to Hythe from the Cross by going due east along which used to be the old coach road between Hythe and London. The distance is about a mile and a half. All these roads are signposted.

INGOLDSBY COUNTRY
Starting point: the Black Horse *on bus routes 102 & 16 (A260)*
Distance: approximately 5 miles
Type of walk: field paths and lanes

From the *Black Horse* northward to Selsted the road is quite straight and it is believed to be part of a Roman highway. Swingfield Minnis was open common land in bygone days and it provided a training ground for the troops gathered to resist Napoleon. It was also the happy hunting ground for footpads and highwaymen.

A few hundred yards beyond the *Black Horse* there is a grass road on the left opposite the turning to Little Foxholt Farm. This passes near Hoad Farm which may once have been connected with the Preceptory of the Knights of St John, for the old building has a door and windows of ecclesiastical design. The grass track joins

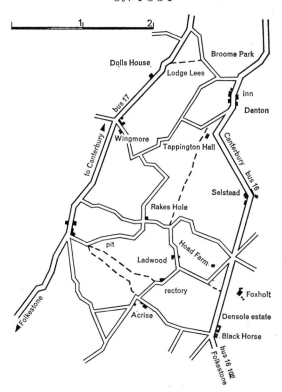

a narrow road which winds downhill. At the road junction half a
mile further on turn right to pass Ladwood Farm and reach another
cross-road at Rakeshole, once called Rakes Hall. The road on the
left is signposted to Elham, that on the right to Swingfield; between
there is a bridle road running almost due north along a deep valley
which in summer is full of wild flowers. The man orchid used to be
common on these chalk hills, but even this shallow soil is being
cultivated now. Under the beech trees round Denton the white
helleborine holds its own, and the twayblade, spotted orchis and the
fragrant orchis live on the edge of the woodland.

At any time in the year the greater spotted woodpecker and the
treecreeper may be found in the old trees, which also provide
attractive homes for little owls. In spring and summer a lucky find
would be the wryneck, but this bird is becoming rare. Rare, too, in
the insect work is the duke of burgundy *Hamearia lucina*, but it has

been seen in this district, so also has the ringlet butterfly *Aphantopus hyperanthus*.

The path skirts Gatteridge Farm and passes behind Tappington Hall Farm. This is a most interesting Tudor building which was the manor house of the Barham family and formed the background of the *Ingoldsby Legends*. It was said to be haunted by the uneasy spirits of two brothers, one a royalist and the other a follower of Cromwell. They met on the staircase there, and one man died at the hand of his brother.

The footpath joins the road opposite Denton Court, and the thirteenth-century church, which has been extensively restored, stands in the grounds. The village lies a few hundred yards along the road on the left. It is a well-kept and attractive place with tudor houses and a comfortable inn which is called the *Jackdaw*, in memory of the unhappy bird of Rheims who stole the Cardinal's ring and lost all his feathers as a punishment.

At the far end of the street a road branches off to the left. It is signposted to Lodge Lees, and by keeping to the right-hand curve it is possible to enjoy a delightful walk across the edge of Broome Park, a lovely wooded area, once the property of Lord Kitchener, and so to go on through Walderchain Wood to reach the Canterbury road (B2065) below Breach Downs near two cottages. Bus 17 passes hourly. Half a mile towards Folkestone on the right there is a most original and attractive tea garden named the *Doll's House*. This is just opposite a very old building with church type windows which was possibly a halting place for pilgrims who journeyed to Canterbury.

LYNSORE VALLEY
Starting point: the Rose & Crown *on Stelling Minnis (Bus 18)*
Distance: approximately 5 miles
Type of walk: woods and open land

Stelling lies at the centre of one of the loveliest areas in East Kent. The word *Minnis* has been taken to mean open common land where building is restricted, the fields unfenced and the pasturage open to the animals belonging to the isolated houses which were scattered over quite a wide area. The land here is largely covered by bracken and gorse, and when this is enriched by the purple willow herb it presents a striking picture. Some building is now being permitted on the outskirts of the common.

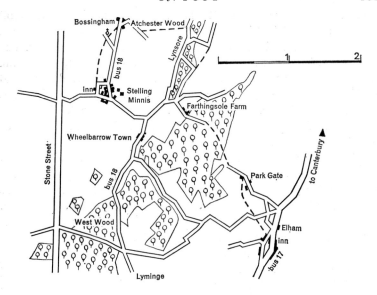

The Minnis is bounded on the west by the great Roman highway of Stone Street, and the church stands alone in massive grandeur half a mile off the common. It is an old building going back to the thirteenth century and is visible for miles around. Lovely conifer woods belonging to the Forestry Commission cover the hills on the south beyond Wheelbarrow Town, a quaint hamlet with this strange name of unknown origin. A fine windmill marks the edge of the open land.

The country on the east of Stelling is heavily wooded with broadleaved trees, notably the whitebeam and the oak. The valleys run from north to south, and so are sheltered from the cold east wind.

Opposite the garage at the entrance to Bossingham at the northern limit of the common is a side road which comes to an end after about a mile, and which is signposted *no through road*. From the point where this road turns sharply right there is a wide path on the left downhill through Atchester Wood. Wild orchids abound here, together with the livelong or sedum, and the delicate wood vetch. The old deciduous trees are attractive to the green woodpecker at all times of the year, and coal tits, too, find them to their liking. On Forestry Commission land the larches provide cones for the crossbills, and nesting places for goldcrests.

The path crosses a field past a line of pylons and emerges on a by-road to Lynsore Bottom. This is a beautiful road, its hedges full of plants of botanical interest, but the lanes tunnelling up through Fryarne Park Wood on the east are very confusing to strangers. The easiest way is not to take the lane up beside the chalk pit, but to walk a few hundred yards south and to take a very narrow and steep road which bends to the right at the top of the hill. Half a mile along this road the way divides. One lane goes downhill back to Stelling, while one turns left to follow a circuitous course to Bladbean. These roads are signposted. Between them is a lane to Farthingsole Farm. After passing the house and going through two gates the track winds down through the woods, to climb eventually very sharply out of the valley and reach Park Gates, a beautiful tudor house. From this point there is a signposted lane down to Elham and the 17 bus stop. This last part of the walk may be shortened by crossing a stile on the right at the top of the hill above Elham. The field path goes round the sports field and reaches the village near the *Rose & Crown*, and the *Abbot's Fireside*.

This is a delightful walk off the beaten track and is possible at all times of the year. The woods near Farthingsole Farm are especially interesting for their wide variety of insect life and for the birds which find the thick bushes conducive to safe nesting. In spring the dainty butterfly the orange tip *Anthocharis cardamines* flits in the clearings, and the rare white admiral *Limenitis camilla* has been seen here, while the spruce trees provide shelter and food for countless numbers of dwarf pug moths.

The path through Atchester Wood is loam over clay and it can be very muddy. In the valleys round Park Gates may be found a variety of wild orchids including the tiny musk orchis now becoming rare, as more and more of the chalk uplands are used for growing crops.